About this book

Blinkers is an informed personal account which provides a fascinating insight into how science has been used, and misused, as a tool to shape our present understanding of our world. The book clearly shows how both scientific evidence and methodology can be manipulated to influence events supporting those agendas for which the outcome has been predetermined. It is a thought-provoking and extremely enjoyable read which explains the pursuit of science in both historical and cultural contexts from which we should learn lessons regarding the impact of science as a tool to shape human destiny. The book is a vital read for all those interested in the communication of science.

Stephen Ham, Director of King Edward VI
Grammar School Science College, Chelmsford

The book by Charles Pasternak illustrates the general syndrome of scientific ignorance in our society and its impact on economical, social and political aspects. Very logical and effective uses of facts and historical events, in the context of fair and insightful personal interpretations, help to highlight the importance for the next generations to have better understanding of science and technology in order for better society and economy. It will be a great book not only for scientists but also for politicians, lawyers, administrators and more.

Wanjin Hong, Professor and Deputy Director Cancer and Developmental
Cell Biology Division, Institute of Molecular and Cell Biology, Singapore

All his life, Charles Pasternak has studied biochemistry, a quite respectable branch of modern science. However, one day the genes of his genius uncle, Russian poet, writer and philosopher Boris Pasternak, revolt against the conventions of Charles Pasternak's everyday inner world. As a result, he writes this book, pronouncing 'unpalatable truths' concerning the narrowness of the traditional scientific approach and the fantastic credulity of mankind. The book is really very, very interesting!

Vladimir Petrovich Skulachev, Academician of the Russian Academy of
Sciences, and Director of the Belozersky Institute of Physico-Chemical
Biology, Moscow State University

It is obvious to me that essentially widespread scientific ignorance prompted Charles Pasternak to write this book. He has used the word 'Blinkers' very thoughtfully. Blinkered people follow a straight course without taking note of the happenings around them. In this book Charles Pasternak has focused on blinkering with respect to scientific issues. I find this book very interesting and objective, and aimed at the assessment of huge problems faced by mankind today. The author has tried to analyse and evaluate these problems based on scientific, religious and historical facts in a very much unbiased manner; he has not even spared politics. I immensely enjoyed going through the book. It is relevant to scientists as well as non-scientists and the common man alike. I fully endorse the view of Charles Pasternak that there is a necessity to take science to the masses in order to make this world a better place to live. I am sure that the wealth of knowledge contained in this book will inspire everyone, including so-called intellectuals. Prof Pasternak certainly deserves appreciation for vividly bringing out, through this book, the relationship between events and their impact on society, in a thought-provoking manner.

Lalji Singh, Bhatnagar Fellow [CSIR] and former Director,
Centre for Cellular and Molecular Biology, Hyderabad, India

Simultaneously thoughtful and entertaining, this well-researched yet thoroughly accessible book illuminates the costs and consequences of scientific illiteracy and what can be done about it. Through copious examples from history to the present day, Pasternak's clear-headed prose shows how a lack of understanding of basic principles of probability and statistics has lost wars and allowed the general public to be manipulated by politicians, the media, and scientists as well. This book should be a clarion-call for science education.

Michael W. Quick, Executive Vice Dean and Professor of Biological Sciences,
College of Letters, Arts & Sciences, University of Southern California, Los Angeles

Ignorance or misunderstanding of science is endemic, not only among the public but -- more disquietingly -- among politicians and the media. This is serious because more and more of the decisions that we make as citizens, or which politicians make on our behalf, have a scientific aspect. We all need a better feel for what science can and cannot tell us, and a realistic perception of risk and uncertainty. In this highly readable book, Charles Pasternak deploys his expertise and long experience to offer a robust defence of science, enlivened by interesting anecdotes and examples from many fields. He offers important lessons for scientists, for politicians, and for those engaged with the media. All will enjoy and benefit from this stimulating and well-written book.

Lord [Martin] Rees, recently President of the Royal Society,
Master of Trinity College, Cambridge

About the author

Charles A. Pasternak is a biochemist and founding Director of the Oxford International Biomedical Centre. His previous academic experience has included research and teaching posts at the universities of Oxford, London (St George's Medical School), Yale and California (UCSD Medical School). While at St George's Medical School, he was founder and Chairman of the Department of Biochemistry, which he later expanded into the Department of Cellular and Molecular Sciences.

Charles Pasternak is acclaimed for his pioneering work in membrane research and is a tireless promoter of international collaboration, working with UNESCO, IUBMB and universities worldwide. He is the author of a number of books and founded *Bioscience Reports* of which he was for 28 years editor-in-chief. He has recently turned his attention to communicating scientific subjects to a broader readership.

Author photographed by Jenny Matthews

Also by the author

Also by Charles Pasternak

Quest: The Essence of Humanity (2003; paperback 2004)
The Molecules Within Us: Our Body in Health and Disease (1998)
Introduction to Human Biochemistry (1979)
The Biochemistry of Differentiation (1970)

Among books edited by Charles Pasternak are

Access Not Excess. The search for better nutrition (2011)
What Makes Us Human? (2007)

Blinkers

Scientific ignorance and evasion

Blinkers

Scientific ignorance and evasion

The case for science

By Charles Pasternak

SMITH-GORDON

Published by Smith-Gordon
In cooperation with Nishimura

In North America contact Linda P. Jones, Enfield Publishing and Distribution Co Inc,
PO Box 699, Enfield, NH 03748, USA
Tel: +1 603 632 7377 Fax: 603 632 5611

Sales enquiries except for the countries listed below may be directed to:
mlevens@smith-gordon.com
Postal address: Smith-Gordon, Units 1-3, The Ermine Centre, Hurricane Close,
Huntingdon, Cambridgeshire PE29 6XX, United Kingdom
For special editions contact publisher@smithgordon.com

In Japan contact Nishimura Company Limited, 1-754-39 Asihimashi-dori,
Niigata-shi 950 Japan
Tel: +81 03-3239-7671 Tokyo and +81 025-223-2388 Niigata
Email: info@nishimurashoten.co.jp www.nishimurashoten.co.jp

In South East Asia contact Alkem Company Pte Ltd. 1 Penjuru Close,
Singapore 608617, Singapore
Tel: +65 6265 6666; Fax: + 65 6261 7875
Email: chubong@alkem.com.sg

©2012
First published in Great Britain 2012
Smith-Gordon, Smith-Gordon, Units 1-3, The Ermine Centre, Hurricane Close,
Huntingdon, Cambridgeshire PE29 6XX, United Kingdom

Dedicated to the memory of Anne McLaren, DBE FRS,
scientist, colleague, friend. She well understood
the harm of scientific ignorance, and would,
I hope, have appreciated this book

Contents

Acknowledgements

I am grateful to Cynthia Beall, Alan Bond, Katharine Birbalsingh, Christopher Booker, Francis Collins, John Ellis, Nick Gibb, George Guise, Nick Jelley, Nathan Lewis, Martin Manning, John Meakin, Denis Noble, Marianne Ødegaard, Terence Ryan, Victor Whittaker and Frans de Waal for valuable information, to David Smith of Annette Green Literary Agency for suggesting the topic, to Eldred Smith-Gordon for having the courage to publish my sometimes controversial views, and to Iris Gruenebaum for meticulous proof-reading and to Kasia Lewis for keeping the Oxford International Biomedical Centre ticking over while I dabbled with *Blinkers*. I am grateful to the staff of the British Library and the London Library for their constant support. The peace and quiet of Genny and (the late) Nick Walker's home in Cortijo Grande, Almeria, and that of Camilla and Gian Ludovico de Martino di Montegiordano in Amantea, Calabria, over successive years has made writing this book a pleasure.

The author and publisher thank the authors of the illustrations in this book. The sources are given on pages 25, 31, 60, 80 and 83. On pages 40-42 we are grateful to Johns Hopkins University Press for permission to illustrate an example of fake ESP from *Debunked!* By Georges Charpak and Henri Broch Translated from French by Bart K Holland, 2004. See Bibliography, page 155.

Foreword
by Sir Harry Kroto, Nobel Laureate

ALTHOUGH Science and Technology have transformed our daily lives out of all recognition, it is clear that the general level of appreciation is depressingly low and the intrinsic level of understanding in many cases dangerous. The state of science and mathematics teaching is clearly abysmal, not just in the West but on a global scale as witnessed by the upsurge in efforts to undermine the veracity of Darwinian Evolution – a theory which finds confirmation in countless observations and underpins the whole of biology and the medical sciences. Numerous articles have drawn attention to this problem and the recent one in the science journal *Nature* [465: 525-6, 2010] is cited in Chapter 6 of this book.

This poor level of scientific understanding becomes ever more frightening as people in positions of responsibility (and anti-humanitarian irresponsibility) become involved with decisions involving ever more powerful technologies about which they know little and understand less. The result is that most politicians, journalists and others who influence policy and the views of the public, are ignorant of the science behind some of the most important issues of our day. The disparaging comments by people with high (UK) media profiles such as comedian Billy Connolly and TV personality Jeremy Clarkson, as well as the tirade against mathematics teaching in schools by a former editor of *The Times*, are clear indications of the disgraceful situation in the UK. Similar attitudes are to be found in the US where political leaders propagate derisive anti-scientific and anti-mathematics views among young and vulnerable students. The level of scientific understanding to be found in Internet blogs on controversial issues such as climate change, genetically modified crops and Darwinian Evolution are truly frightening examples of the problem. They should be recognised fundamentally, not as attacks on specific issues as they appear on the surface, but on scientific method itself, which is the only philosophical construct we have to determine 'Truth' with any degree of reliability.

I have spent many years exploring ways in which science education might be improved on a global scale and have constantly tried to improve our approaches to revealing not just the excitement of scientific discovery but also deeply beautiful, fascinating and always amazing ways in which the natural and physical worlds work. For young people this involves ways to make hands-on approaches to creating things as much a 'fun' exercise as a learning device. It is arguably the most important skill that teachers of science must possess. Charles Pasternak, who has spent a lifetime engaged in science teaching, addresses the key science education issues admirably in this highly engaging book: *Blinkers: scientific ignorance and evasion*. He draws attention to the key topics and presents them in a light, entertaining and highly effective way. I enjoyed reading this book, and am delighted to recommend it to the widest possible audience: from lawmakers and the media, to teachers, students and other professionals and of course to the public at large.

CHAPTER 1

Scientific ignorance: two cultures still?

IT was a lovely spring afternoon in 1984 and Chequers was looking its best. The daffodils and narcissi had just come out. Their tint of pale gold and white made a pleasing contrast with the reddish stone of the building. This splendid Elizabethan mansion (Lady Mary Grey, youngest sister of the unfortunate Lady Jane Grey, was incarcerated here for a while), nestling below the Chiltern Hills in Buckinghamshire, had been donated to the British nation in 1921 by its owner, Arthur Lee. He realised that prime ministers of the day were no longer landed gentry, and so lacked a week-end residence. One good turn deserves another, and his generosity earned him the title of Lord Lee of Farnham. On this day in 1984, Margaret Thatcher was handing out tea and cakes to her visitors. The guests were all scientists, assembled to advise the prime minister on their latest discoveries. A former colleague of mine, who was one of the group, found himself sitting next to Thatcher's most cerebral cabinet minister, Keith Joseph. Joseph did not trade banalities about the coal miners' strike that had just erupted on account of the proposed closure of certain pits [1]. Instead he remarked 'These molecules you talk about: what exactly are they? If I put some in a box, will they still be there in 10 days', or in 10 years', time?' The question revealed an apparent ignorance of scientific reality, namely that all matter is made up of molecules – whether it is the wood of the box or the air inside it – and that molecules remain intact unless they are changed to other molecules by chemical reactions. As a classical scholar Keith Joseph probably knew that Democritus had postulated the indivisibility of matter and coined the word atom some 2400 years ago, but he had failed to connect the two. Yet Joseph was Secretary of State for Education *and Science*.

Already in 1916, a former member of Gladstone's last government had warned the Privy Council that 'not only are our highest Ministers of State ignorant of science, but the same defect runs through almost all the public departments of the Civil Service. It is nearly universal in the House of Commons. ... Our success now in the very difficult time of reorganization after the war depends largely on the possession of our leaders and administrators of the scientific method and the scientific habit of mind' [2]. This was echoed a year later by a prescient scientist who recognised that: 'The fate of nations hangs literally on the issue of contemporary experiments in the laboratory; but those who govern the Empire are quite content to know nothing of all this' and that 'Uncomfortable as the reflection may be, it is not to be denied that the countries in which science has already attained the greatest influence and recognition in public affairs are Germany and Japan, where the opinions of the ignorant are not invited' [3]. Not surprising, as the seeds had been sown in Germany much earlier. Already in 1642 the duchies of Saxe-Coburg and Saxe-Gotha included natural science and arithmetic among the subjects to be taught at elementary level [4]. Whereas in early twentieth century Britain, science was viewed as 'some kind of Germanic vice', which would only foster 'the very spirit against which the war was being fought' [5].

Yet '… as an instrument of mind-training, and even of liberal education, [the teaching of science] seems to me to have a far higher value than is usually conceded to it by humanists. To direct the imagination to the infinitely great and the infinitely small, to vistas of time in which a thousand years are as one day; to the tremendous forces imprisoned in minute particles of matter; to the amazing complexity of the mechanism by which the organs of the human body perform their work; to analyse the light which has travelled for centuries from some distant star; to retrace the history of the earth and the evolution of its inhabitants – such studies cannot fail to elevate the mind, and only prejudice will disparage them. They promote also a fine respect for truth and fact, for order and outline'. Who do you think said that? No, not the president of the US Academy of Sciences or his counterpart at the Royal Society in the UK, nor the latest Nobel Laureate in one of the sciences. These words were written *ninety years* ago, by a *cleric:* by W R Inge, the admittedly exceptional Dean of St Paul's Cathedral in London [6]. One could be forgiven for thinking that we are going backwards.

To the author and physicist C P Snow, writing in the late 1950s, the situation exemplified a lack of understanding between the two cultures: that of the arts and that of the sciences [7]. As Keith Joseph's remark showed, not much had changed since Snow's analysis. Today, a further quarter of a century on, and there is still a remarkable lack of scientific know-how among non-scientists. Judges in criminal cases seem incapable of understanding the rudiments of probability. Lawyers have difficulty in coping with DNA technology. The last president of the United States had difficulty comprehending global warming, and his counterpart in South Africa for long denied any connection between HIV infection and AIDS. Some time ago the Parliamentary Under Secretary of State for Schools and Learners in the UK authorised schools to teach 'intelligent design', despite rejection of this ridiculous idea by the Roman Catholic Church itself [8]. *The Daily Mail* considered genetically-modified crops to constitute a threat of 'Frankenstein' dimensions, and the manufacturers of health products throughout the world persuade millions of people to spend their last penny on pills and capsules that are without benefit of any sort.

As an individual, of course, you are entitled to live according to your own precepts. Those who don't wish to embrace scientific advances may avoid them. The most technologically sophisticated country in the world is home to communities that are frozen in the lifestyle of the early eighteenth century. The Amish, who live not just in Pennsylvania [9], but in Ohio, Indiana, Delaware and New York as well as in Canada, eschew the use of electric light and heating, automobiles and aircraft, telephones and computers. Around them, the heirs of their erstwhile neighbour in Philadelphia who introduced electricity [10] to America in the late eighteenth century, have not ceased their quest for new-fangled ideas. Yet the Amish enjoy as contented a life as their fellows: the rate of suicide among them is less than half that in the USA as a whole [11].

Your beliefs are surely your own as well. If you wish to consider the earth to be the centre of our solar system, that is your prerogative. Anyway, doesn't everyone refer to the dawn of another day as sunrise, and its close as sunset [12]? Yet for most of us, scientific ignorance is incompatible with the world in which we live. The Amish may be able to disregard modern technology (though I suspect their grasp of science is considerably sounder than that of astrology-believing folk in San Francisco or South Kensington [13]), and so may the inhabitants of Papua New Guinea, Amazonia or the Kalahari Desert [14]. But if you live in today's world of robotic surgery and liposuction, of vaccine-containing bananas and hormone-enriched rice, of wind farms and liquor-powered cars, of faster travel and slower ageing, you'd better know something of the science behind it. Not just if you're a law maker or a policy advisor, a teacher or someone about to go on jury service, but as a concerned member of the community in which you live. For in a democracy it is you, not ignorant politicians or zealous scientists, who should be taking decisions about the implementation of novel technology. The issues of stem-cell manipulation and regenerative medicine, of planting genetically-modified crops next to your back garden, of triple vaccines, of allowing your DNA profile and its genetic implications to be seen by insurance companies – all these whirlwind changes to our way of life, should be debated by a scientifically savvy public. Acceptance of two cultures in the developed world is no longer an option.

In any case, Snow was wrong on one point. A large number of those brought up in the humanities indeed display a proud ignorance of science, and consider scientists as boors or nerds, but the reverse is not true. Snow himself was not the only scientist who became a novelist. Many display an ability to engage simultaneously in science and the arts. Benjamin Franklin ('the most accomplished American of his age and the most influential in inventing the type of society America would become' [15]) was a prolific writer on political and social issues as well as inventing the lightning rod, bifocals, the circulating stove and a simple odometer, the Russian composer Alexander Borodin was a successful, professional research chemist who merely later turned to music, William Herschel, conversely, was a talented musician who only subsequently took up astronomy [16], Humphrey Davy was a brilliant chemist [17], inventor of the miner's safety lamp and President of the Royal Society who wrote poetry throughout his life, Anton Chekhov and Somerset Maugham trained as doctors before beginning literary careers (as had Keats), the astronomer Fred Hoyle wrote as many works of fiction as he did of science, Robert Oppenheimer, who 'almost as an aside, postulated (correctly) the existence of black holes in 1939' and then directed the Manhatten Project that created the world's first atomic bomb in 1945, also wrote poetry [18], Manfred Eigen, Nobel Laureate in Chemistry, is an accomplished musician, and so on. These men, it is true, were endowed with an outstanding intellect that enabled them to straddle the two cultures. Also, some of the examples quoted are to be expected, in so far as mathematical and musical ability appear to be linked - 'hard-wired' in our brains - but that merely makes my point. A N Whitehead [19] considered poetry and science to depend on the same mental ability: the organisation of one's thoughts. But over the years I have come into contact with a large number of ordinary scientists, each of whose spare time has been spent in music, painting or writing: they are as enthusiastic and as competent about their art as anyone trained solely in the humanities. Is that not your experience also?

While a classical education was considered, well into the twentieth century, to be the best way train Britain's bureaucrats, administrators, politicians and empire-builders, others have pointed to its defects. A remark made already almost two hundred years ago is typical. A friend of John Constable, writing to the artist in 1825, quoted the view expressed by the author of a *History of England*, that 'our classical education ... stunts originality, contracts the mind, and makes men knowing only in *words*' [20]. Anne McLaren, a brilliant scientist in the field of human embryology, to whose memory this book is dedicated, once told me that she considered *all* formal education, beyond the age of ten or so, to be detrimental to the spirit of unfettered enquiry among the young. Education needs to be more carefully thought-out.

In any case, the process of creativity is common to science and art. Science strives to explain nature, art to illuminate it. Scientists and artists are each driven by their innate curiosity to produce something novel: a more accurate description of the world, a more pleasing melody, picture or literary tract. Coleridge recognised this, and his friend Humphrey Davy (whom he tried to interest in setting up his laboratory in the Lake District, along with his companions Wordsworth and Southey), considered that 'Imagination, as well as the reason, is necessary to perfection in the philosophic mind. A rapidity of combination, a power of perceiving analogies, and of comparing them by facts, is the creative source of discovery' [21]. A scientist of my acquaintance illustrates this well: he was a most cultured man, with a voracious appetite for knowledge. The background to his achievements was this. For over two decades during the second half of the twentieth century, biochemists had sought a 'high-energy chemical intermediate' molecule. This was assumed to link the process of respiration, by which foodstuffs like carbohydrate, fat and protein are oxidised in the body, to the synthesis of a molecule called ATP. It is ATP that then drives all energy-requiring processes in the body like muscle contraction, the re-synthesis of carbohydrate, fat and protein, and so on [22]. Along comes Peter Mitchell [23], a maverick scientist who apes Robert Boyle and Isaac Newton by carrying out his researches in the tranquillity of his own home. In Mitchell's case this was an imposing house in Cornwall, far away from the busy laboratories of Cambridge and Edinburgh.

Like some country squire, Mitchell ran a home farm, bottled spring water and minted silver coins [24]. But every morning he sat down with his long-term collaborator Jennifer Moyle in order to discuss the results of yesterday's experiments and to plan that day's. By dint of his creative instinct, with a minimum of experimental evidence, Mitchell came to the conclusion that there is no 'high-energy chemical intermediate' at all: energy for the synthesis of ATP comes from transport processes across the membranes that lie within every cell. The critics of this theory pooh-poohed Mitchell's proposal and stuck to their preconceived idea about a chemical intermediate. In his study overlooking the lush Cornish countryside, Mitchell kept a map of the world. He stuck a green pin into the location of a new supporter, red pins into those of his opponents. Red pins greatly outnumbered green ones. But Mitchell had tenacity as well as the creative urge and he persevered. He proposed new arguments and devised novel experiments to rebuff his detractors. Gradually the colour of the pins began to change from red to green. Not until December of 1978, as Peter and his wife Helen, together with Jennifer Moyle, boarded a plane for Stockholm, did it dawn on the majority of 'high-energy chemical intermediate' supporters that they might have been wrong. Mitchell's name was the sole one cited for the Nobel Prize in Chemistry that year, a rather unusual distinction in the case of an award in science.

If the two-culture concept applies to any group of people, it might perhaps do so in the case of the technician versus the artisan. But in truth the division is not between science and art at all. It is between the well-educated (including a grasp of science) and the poorly-educated. In France, where science and mathematics are compulsory subjects alongside philosophy in the *baccalauréat*, the two-culture phenomenon barely exists. Nor is it apparent in Germany, other northern European countries, or the USA. So much of the discord between science and art is illusory.

Mental blinkers

Today's scientifically naïve persons – whether politicians, lawyers, journalists, television presenters or lay members of society – often *think* they understand a scientific issue, without in fact doing so. School teachers and academics appear to be the exception: they tend to admit their ignorance, occasionally with a touch of pride. Certain people, and they can include scientists themselves, deliberately misinterpret or evade a scientific fact. That is why I have used the words blinkers ('blinders' in some countries) in my title. A horse that is blinkered will follow a straight course because it is not distracted by anything that happens on either side. Humans wear mental blinkers. In a novel entitled *Blinkers. A Romance of the Preconceived Idea* [25], the author shows how the love between two young people proves to be ephemeral because it is based on a preconceived idea – held by each – that turns out to have been wrong. Here I show how many preconceived notions about science and the world have likewise proved to be erroneous. Part of the problem lies, as Goethe had recognised, in the fact that science 'frequently – even normally – contradicts our senses' [26], a view more recently expressed as the 'unnatural nature of science' [27]. But wilful denial of the evidence also plays a part.

Blinkered leaders

Mental blinkers, of course, are nothing new. Throughout the ages, nations have been blinkered to their neighbours' capabilities. During the third century BC, the Qin of northern China called their southern neighbours Han, which had a pejorative meaning at that time. The Han referred to the Qin as 'barbarian weakling', and proved their point by overthrowing them in 206 BC. The Romans likewise considered the tribes living beyond their northern frontier as barbarians [28] and suffered a similar shock in 476 AD. The British failed to consider the consequences of a direct tax on the American colonists in 1765; worse, they followed it up two years later with an even more unpopular tax on tea and other imported goods. Their surprise at the insurrection that followed was matched only by their shock at its outcome. Yet they should have known that 'Any general in the world other than General Howe would have beaten General Washington; and any general in the world other than General Washington would have beaten General Howe' [29]. The Mughal emperor Bahadur Shah II was blinkered into inaction during the Indian mutiny of 1857, as a result of which a once-proud dynasty fizzled out ignominiously [30]. A similar fate befell the Chinese empire around this time. Despite finding themselves unable to win against a handful of foreigners during the Opium Wars of 1839-42 and 1856-60, the Qing did little to modernise their great nation – the most inventive that the world had ever seen during preceding centuries – and it sank to oblivion in 1911. Though the underlying cause was different, the demise of the Qing was as final as that of the Qin in 206 BC.

You might take the view that all empires last only so long: they are destined to decline at some point anyway. John Glubb put the period during which empires are at their height as, on average, no more than 200 to 250 years. The dynasty of the Qing, for example, was maintained for 265 years; that of the Mughals for a further 47 years. But each had begun its slide to extinction considerably sooner. The Roman empire, that was in continuous existence for 450 years (again without effective government towards the end), is at one end of this longevity scale; the Seljuq dynasty of Persia, at 100 years, is at the other. The 1500 years of Roman rule in the east hardly counts as that of a thriving empire. The Venetian Republic, that lasted successfully for 1000 years, succeeded only because its rulers, the Doges, were elected by an extremely intricate mechanism [31] that brought fresh blood to the state every 10 years or so. 'Apart from the casualties caused by wars, pioneering and emigration, national decadence is probably largely attributable to too long a duration of wealth and power. The nation gradually, but unconsciously, assumes that pre-eminence is automatically its due, without any obligation to toil or struggle ... Eight or nine generations seem to be sufficient to change the hardy and enterprising pioneers into the idle and querulous citizens of the welfare state' [32]. The author of this argument, John Glubb, incidentally, is a good example of someone who successfully spanned two cultures: that of the soldier (he trained as an engineer) and that of the historian. Readers may recall his name when I reveal that he was better known as Glubb Pasha, the charismatic leader of the Arab legion between the two world wars. Having turned to writing only at the age of 60, he produced 22 books (largely about the Arab character) over the next 25 years. His remark about the lack of 'obligation to toil or struggle' as empires decline, has consonance with Arnold Toynbee's view that the very emergence of civilisations depends on overcoming detrimental circumstances, not on exploiting favourable environments [33]. The complacency of emperors that leads to their running out of steam is a blinkered outlook. Current dumbing-down, in education and art, is likely to lead to a similar decline in a nation's spirit [34].

More recent examples of a nation losing out because of a preconceived idea may be cited. They include one at the beginning of World War II, and one at its end. In 1940 the French considered the emplacements of the Maginot Line, that they had constructed over the past 10 years against the threat of another German invasion – this time by tanks – impenetrable. It may well have been so, but their wily neighbour simply avoided it by breaking through at the point where the line continued north through Belgium, and then heading south unimpeded. In 1944 it was clear to the German High Command that an allied invasion across the Channel was inevitable. They assumed that the landings would be across the shortest stretch of water from southern England, on the shores of the Pas de Calais. Their surmise was strengthened by the many reports of a massive concentration of troops on the English side of the Channel. The arrival of the invaders along a 20-mile stretch of beach on the northern coast of Normandy, from Arromanches in the west to the river Orme in the east, took them completely by surprise: the intelligence reports received by the German High Command proved to have been fakes, deliberately planted by Eisenhower's counter-intelligence units. It was actually the second time the Germans had been fooled by allied trickery: in 1943, prior to the invasion of Sicily from North Africa, which was the obvious route to southern Europe, operation 'Mincemeat' deceived Hitler into thinking that allied troops were heading for Greece.

By 1944, of course, the war was already lost for Germany. The tide had begun to turn, though the consequences were initially not apparent, by two events in 1941. The first was the result of Hitler's blinkered thinking that he could defeat the Soviet Union and expand Germany's frontiers eastwards. He broke the non-aggression treaty that existed between the two countries (reneging on signed pacts was second nature to him) and launched his attack on 22 June 1941. Hitler was a pretty blinkered man: his thousand-year Reich lasted precisely 12 years. The second event was Japan's attack on Pearl Harbor on 7 December 1941. Another blinkered decision: did Japan really believe it could knock the United States out by a single attack on its navy? America's entry into the fray four days later effectively sealed Germany's fate, and subsequently that of Japan, too. Other examples exist, but I believe I have made my point: to consider your neighbour as inferior to yourself is dangerous. Yet it is practically 'hard-wired' in our brains: chimpanzees and bonobos [35], our closest ancestral relatives, exhibit just such behaviour [36].

Cultures that are blinkered in other ways often finish up badly. The inhabitants of the Easter Islands are a prime example. Their ancestors, who set off from south-east Asia some thousand years ago, were clever enough to have sailed 10,000 miles against the prevailing wind, and to have found a small volcanic island, blessed with fresh water lakes, on which to settle. These seafarers then displayed the most amazing technological skill by carving the huge statues, known as *moai*, out of the local rock. Only the Egyptian Sphinx and the colossal heads carved by the Olmec – the earliest civilisation of the New World – come close in craftsmanship. Yet the Easter Islanders nearly became extinct in the seventeenth century. It wasn't the 'little ice age' that began around 1650, that did for them. It was their own folly in cutting down the forests of palm and broad-leaved trees in order to make yet more boats for fishing. Just as the enterprising spirit of emperors dwindles after ten or so generations, so the innovative streak among a group of islanders turned to thoughtlessness. The ecosystem couldn't respond fast enough, and the Easter Islanders appear to have run out of a supply of timber for boat-building, and hence of their staple protein diet, fish. Birds, the islanders' other major source of food, perished at the same time because there was nowhere for them to nest [37]. As will become apparent in Chapter 4, politicians are currently blinkered by advocating the use of arable land in order to produce biofuels: a resulting world food shortage is unfolding before our eyes.

Blinkering the people
Rulers, as well as religious leaders, have for centuries deliberately exploited the blinker principle to keep their people in check. Removing blinkers was not allowed. It brought Galileo nothing but trouble in the seventeenth century, and sent millions to the gulag in the twentieth [38]. Until the late nineteenth century, the masses in Great Britain, even of enlightened Europe and the United States, were denied any education whatsoever. It was the Elementary Education Act of 1870 that introduced formal and compulsory education for children in England and Wales (in Scotland this happened much earlier), but only up to the age of 12 or 13. Not until 1944 was secondary education made free (and compulsory) to all in Great Britain. This represented a typically British malaise: in Prussia, elementary education had been made compulsory already in the eighteenth century by Frederick the Great; in France, Denmark, Sweden and other European nations, as well as in the USA, universal education preceded that in England by more than 50 years. The young on English soil had been kept blinkered on account of three factors. First, if children were to spend their time in school, who would work in the factories and the fields? These critics had forgotten Martin Luther's views, more than three centuries earlier. To the objection that 'we cannot bring up all our children to be students for we need them at home to work' he answered: 'I ask only that boys shall attend such schools as I have in view, an hour or two a day, and spend the rest of their time at home, or in learning some trade … thus both matters will be cared for together.' In the same way 'little girls may easily find time enough to go to school an hour a day, and yet do all their household duties …' [39].

Second, who would pay for all this education? As the future prime minister Lord Salisbury had pointed out, 'If in addition to the other burdens that land has to bear, you assume that it should also bear the expenses of national education, you will create a spirit of resistance which will secure for your system an amount of unpopularity which no improvement you may make in education will be able to counterbalance' [40]. Arguments about the cost of education were as strongly voiced in the USA as in England. New York Governor Lucius B Robinson said in 1879, in regard to the taxation necessary to finance public high schools, 'When we ... take from one man the money necessary to educate the children of another in arts and sciences, we perpetuate an act of injustice ...' [41].

Third, there was the religious argument: 'The more a man is advanced in human knowledge, the more he is opposed to religion, and is the more deadly enemy to the truth of God' [42]. Moreover education would make the labouring classes 'despise their lot in life, instead of making them good servants in agriculture, and other laborious employments to which their rank in society had destined them; instead of teaching them subordination it would render them factious and refractory ... it would enable them to read seditious pamphlets ... ' [43]. Thus did the preconceived ideas of the ruling class keep their inferiors in ignorance for centuries. It has to be said that their own children were well educated in the 'public' – actually private – schools like Eton and Winchester, Harrow and Westminster. This provided a further reason for the British establishment not to introduce universal education. Have we at last seen an end to blinkers imposed on the young? Not at all. Blinkered science education is only slowly being eradicated in mid-Western America, and it is alive and well in the *madrasahs* of the Islamic world. Education of any sort continues to be denied to girls by the Taliban in areas where they have control.

To illustrate the first of the above remarks, let me remind readers of the attempt by an enlightened group of parents to force an education authority to stop confusing its youth. In 2005, the school officials in the town of Dover, Pennsylvania ordered 'intelligent design', that is an offshoot of divine creationism, to be taught in biology class, alongside evolution. The children's parents, who had the actual teachers on their side, disagreed, and took the officials to court. The parents won. The judge, a devout Lutheran and a Republican appointed by the president of the USA, had clearly disappointed his followers. Yet he was subsequently placed in the list of the world's one hundred most influential men by *Time* magazine [44]. The age-long incompatibility between religious leaders, blinkered by their preconceived ideas, and scientists, exercising their quest for knowledge about the world, might seem to be another case of two cultures. But was it really so?

Few of the Athenian intellectuals of Plato's time believed in the purported deeds of their gods, though they remained superstitious in other ways. Plato 'denied that there was any conflict between reason and traditional Greek piety. There were no compelling proofs for the existence of the Olympian *daimones*, but it was irrational and unintelligent to deny the ancient myths, because like fairy tales, they contained a modicum of truth' [45]. He himself considered the world to have been created by a 'demiurge' of supreme wisdom, and his pupil Aristotle thought of such a figure as an 'unmoved mover': he was aware that everything in the cosmos moves [46]. You could hardly blame them, as there was no scientific evidence to the contrary. Cicero, as sceptical as he was of the gods the Romans took over from the Greeks (along with democracy, architecture and poetry), hedged his bets with the notion of a divine power 'to be found in a principle of reason which pervades the whole of nature' [47]. Not until the sixteenth century did things begin to change.

The enlightenment at this time was based largely on physics, not on biology: on the observations of Copernicus, Galileo and Newton. The Church of Rome may have considered heliocentricity blasphemous, but no one else did. Least of all the scientists themselves. Had not Thomas Aquinas conceded, 300 years earlier, that there is no conflict between reason and faith? Copernicus found no cause to conclude that the earth's movement around the sun indicated an absence of God's hand. On the contrary, 'To know the mighty works of God; to comprehend His wisdom and majesty and power; to appreciate, in degree, the wonderful working of His laws, surely all this must be a pleasing and acceptable mode of worship to the Most High, to whom ignorance cannot be more grateful than knowledge' [48]. Galileo, in a letter defending himself against charges of apostasy, famously said 'I do not feel obliged to believe that the same God who has endowed us with sense, reason and intellect has intended us to forego their use' [49]. Newton published more works on the interpretation of the Bible than on mathematics and physics combined. He was a firm Unitarian and therefore did not believe in the doctrine of the three-fold Trinity. To him, God alone reigns supreme. 'Gravity explains the motions of the planets, but it cannot explain who set the planets in motion. God governs all things and knows all that is or can be done' [50]. His aversion to the Trinity did not prevent him accepting a fellowship at the college of that name in Cambridge when he was appointed Lucasian Professor at the age of 26. There was only one snag. Fellows of colleges needed to be of the Anglican persuasion. Newton would not budge. It took an enlightened monarch, Charles II, to issue a dispensation to enable the young scholar to take up his post. Nineteenth century physicists like Michael Faraday, William Thomson (Lord Kelvin) or James Clerk Maxwell did not allow their scientific insight to impinge on their religious beliefs either.

Today's professional atheists [51] foster the idea of two cultures: one of bigoted religious leaders trying to foist their preconceived ideas on a scientifically naïve public, and one of enlightened *savants* like themselves. They are wrong. The difference is not between religious folk and their irreligious opposites, but again, between well-educated and badly-educated individuals. Religion may be myth, but religious beliefs are not. Pause for a moment to consider why spiritual beliefs – among the well-educated at that – have persisted for four hundred years after Galileo, three hundred years after Newton, two hundred years after Darwin, one hundred years after Einstein. It is because they are almost as hard-wired in our brains as the feeling of superiority over our neighbours.

In this book I focus primarily on blinkering with regard to scientific issues. Some of the blinkers constitute plain ignorance, some entail confusion, others imply an evasion of facts. Technological exploitation of new knowledge, about ourselves and the world we inhabit, is moving so rapidly and so extensively that we can no longer afford a laissez-faire attitude. I shall give examples of blinkers placed on the unsuspecting public by politicians and the media, as well as of blinkers worn by individuals themselves.

Few understand the nature of risk. During the BSE [52] crisis that erupted in Britain in 1986 and continued for a decade, both the agriculture minister and the Chief Medical Officer blithely told the public that beef was safe for everyone to eat. They should not have made this statement, and I shall discuss why in Chapter 2. Risk is an expression of probability and chance. The philosopher A J Ayer distinguished three ways in which we use the word *chance* to refer to judgements of probability [53]:

> *judgements of a priori probability*: 'the chance of throwing double-six with a pair of true dice is one in 36'
> *estimates of actual frequency*: 'there is a slightly better than even chance that any given unborn child will be a boy'
> *judgements of credibility*: 'there is now very little chance that Britain will join the Common Market' [54]

We shall meet examples of all three: *judgements of a priori probability* in relation to the beginning of the world and to particle physics; *estimates of actual frequency* in regard to a couple of murder trials, to road safety, and to various diseases including that caused by eating BSE-tainted beef; and *judgements of credibility* in so far as the millennium bug or Y2K, astrology, ESP and homeopathy are concerned.

The influence that the media exert on our lives cannot be overestimated. In Chapter 3, I shall describe scientifically flawed views regarding the cause of AIDS, the purported menace of genetically-modified (GM) foods, and the supposed hazards of vaccines. Media coverage and manufacturers' plugs often go hand in hand: the consumption of health foods is an example. In several cases, media hype has influenced political decisions.

The converse also occurs: politicians use the media in order to persuade an untutored public of their message. Climate change and passive smoking provide telling instances. They also show how elusive scientists themselves can become when they want their message to be unsullied by awkward facts. Scientists have been equally reluctant to accept some very well established folk medicines (Chapter 4).

The greatest damage that is done to the naïve minds of youngsters is to confuse them with incorrect versions of the world in which they live. I have referred to the attempt by the school board in Dover, Pennsylvania to do so. You don't have to be a blinkered fundamentalist for your views to be at odds with known scientific facts. The beliefs of millions of religious people may have little rational basis, but that does not mean that faith is without benefit. The arrogance of some atheists to deny this shows them to be as bigoted – as blinkered – as the very folk they condemn (Chapter 5).

I have implied that scientifically-educated people might make better politicians than scientifically-blinkered ones. An assessment of this proposal is considered in Chapter 6. If it is indeed possible to remove, once and for all, the blinkers I have described throughout this book, how should we go about it?

The allocation of certain topics to particular chapters is necessarily arbitrary. Some of the subjects examined in Chapter 3 might have been included in Chapter 4, and *vice versa*. This is because the hype of newspapers and television, which are commercially driven, often overlaps with the policies of governments and bureaucrats, which are politically driven. Ignorance of risk (Chapter 2) pervades some of the themes of both Chapters 3 and 4. No matter. My aim is to show that all the issues considered in this book emanate from a common fount: scientific ignorance and preconceived ideas. As we march into the twenty-first century, it is high time to address the problem.

The Earth is some 4 billion years old. 400 million years ago, animals appeared. 40 million years ago, platyrrhines (New World monkeys) split from catarrhines (Old World monkeys). 4 million years ago our ancestors began to walk upright, along the valley of the Great Rift Depression that runs from Ethiopia in east Africa down to Lake Malawi. 400,000 years ago *Homo erectus* was living in caves as far apart as Boxgrove in England, Narmada in India, Zhoukoudian in north east-China and Trinil in Java. 40,000 years ago *Homo sapiens* was following in the tracks of his predecessors and settling throughout Africa, Eurasia and Australia. 4000 years ago he was building cities in Sumeria, pyramids in Egypt and stone circles in Britain. Four hundred years ago Rubens was painting *The Massacre of the Innocents*, Monteverdi was composing madrigals, Shakespeare was writing *King Lear*, and Galileo was observing the moons of Jupiter through a telescope. Forty years ago I was teaching biochemistry to science and medical students. Forty years on, every cell in my body will have turned to dust. Human life is as insignificant as a speck of plankton in the ocean, as ephemeral as the tweet of a sparrow. Yet thanks to my parents who gave me life, I have been able to enjoy my fleeting time on Earth. Thanks to my teachers, who introduced me to science, I have been able to savour its explanations of the world around me: sometimes beautifully simple, sometimes surprisingly complex, often counter-intuitive, always fascinating. To keep this knowledge to myself is selfish. To encourage others to acquire it is the purpose of this book.

Notes

[1]   The strike culminated in the shutting down of the entire coal industry, and a considerable loss of trade union power

[2]   Hannah Gay: *The History of Imperial College London 1907-2007. Higher Education and Research in Science, Technology and Medicine* (Imperial College Press, London, 2007), p 75

[3]   W Bateson, in A C Benson (ed): *Cambridge Essays on Education* (Cambridge University Press, 1917), pp 123 and 131

[4]   T L Jarman: *Europe Landmarks in the History of Education. English Education as part of the European Tradition* (2nd edition John Murray, London, 1963), p 152

[5]   Hannah Gay, ibid, p 97. See [2]

[6]   A C Benson (ed): *Cambridge Essays on Education* (Cambridge University Press, 1917), p 25

[7]   C P Snow: *The Two Cultures and the Scientific Revolution. The Rede Lecture 1959* (Cambridge University Press, Cambridge, 1959)

[8]   The Vatican newspaper *L'Osservatore Romano* published an article in January 2006, arguing that intelligent design is not science; see Damian Thompson: *Counterknowledge. How we surrendered to conspiracy theories, quack medicine, bogus science and fake history* (Atlantic Books, London, 2008), p 33

[9]   'Pennsylvania Dutch' is a misnomer; their language is German – Deutsch – and they are of Swiss-German ancestry

[10]   Benjamin Franklin (see note [15])

[11]   5.5 per 100,000, compared with 12.5 per 100,000 in the rest of the country. See Donald Kraybill: Suicide Patterns in Religious Subculture: The Old Order Amish. (*Int J Moral and Social Studies*: 1, autumn 1985)

[12]   Twenty-five per cent of Americans really believe this to be the case; see www.universalacidblog

[13]   Fifty-two per cent of Europeans consider astrology to be 'rather scientific'; see www.universalacidblog

[14]   Though the Kalahari Bushmen, who have lived here for 20,000 years, are under constant harassment from the modernising government of Botswana (that receives financial support from the European Union): having been evicted from their ancestral territory in 2002, the Bushmen won the right to return in 2006. In 2008, however, Botswana decided to build tourist lodges near ancient water-holes, to which the Bushmen are now being denied access

[15]   Walter Isaacson: *Benjamin Franklin: An American Life* (Simon & Schuster, New York, 2003) p 492

[16]   A talented musician on harpsichord, oboe, organ and violin, as well as a composer of symphonies, concertos and church music. It was only as he approached thirty that he turned seriously to astronomy: building his own telescopes, he discovered the planet Uranus (the first planet to be revealed since Ptolemy), and made fundamental advances in our knowledge of the universe, such as the disc-like structure of the Milky Way, and the realisation of galaxies beyond it. Almost by accident, he also discovered infrared radiation. See Richard Holmes: *The Age of Wonder. How the Romantic*

Generation Discovered the Beauty and Terror of Science (Harper Press, London, 2008) for recent biographical tit-bits of this amazing man

[17]   He discovered nitrous oxide ['laughing gas'] and developed the voltaic battery to isolate the elements sodium and potassium by electrolysis

[18]   Freeman Dyson: *The Scientist as Rebel* (New York Review Books, New York, 2006) pp 229-242

[19]   English mathematician and philosopher, 1861-1947 Barry Mazur (The maths raconteur. *Nature* 483: 405, 2012) considers that maths and literature are driven by the same imaginative impulse; see Apostolos Doxiadis and Barry Mazur: *Circles Disturbed: The Interplay of Mathematics and Narrative* (Princeton University Press, 2012)

[20]   This refers to the views of the historian Sharon Turner (1768-1847; see C R Leslie: *Memoirs of the Life of John Constable* (John Lehmann, London, 1949), p 156

[21]   Richard Holmes: *The Age of Wonder. How the Romantic Generation Discovered the Beauty and Terror of Science* (Harper Press, London, 2008), p 276

[22]   For the movement of limbs, the writhing of the intestines and for the pumping of oxygen by the heart. ATP also provides the energy required for the re-absorption of salt after it has filtered through the kidney, and for the re-synthesis of carbohydrate, fat and protein within the body's cells

[23]   See John Prebble and Bruce Weber: *Wandering in the Gardens of the Mind. Peter Mitchell and the Making of Glynn* (Oxford University Press, Oxford, 2003)

[24]   I recall an occasion when he came to lunch with me at St George's Medical School. As we headed from my office, I put his brief case, which seemed extraordinarily heavy, to one side. 'You can leave it here', I said. 'Oh no, I can't', Peter replied. He explained that the case contained gold bars, which he was taking into the City that day, to sell. Most of his research was funded through the enterprise of a rich uncle, and Mitchell – rightly – did not trust the stock exchange

[25] Horace Annesley Vachell: *Blinkers. A Romance of the Preconceived Idea* (Cassell and Company, Limited, London, 1921)

[26] Richard Holmes: ibid p 247. See [21]

[27] Lewis Wolpert: *The Unnatural Nature of Science* (Faber, London, 1992). Note, in contrast, Jacob Bronowski's book entitled *The Common Sense of Science*, 1951

[28] Originally the word simply meant 'foreigner'

[29] According to a British commentator at the time. Quoted by Gore Vidal: *Inventing a Nation. Washington, Adams, Jefferson* (Yale U Press, New Haven, 2003), p 19

[30] See William Dalrymple: *The Last Mughal. The Fall of a Dynasty, Delhi, 1857* (Bloomsbury, London, 2006)

[31] During the 13th century, for example, 'On the day appointed for the election, the youngest member of the Signoria (the inner council of state) was to pray in St Mark's; then, on leaving the Basilica, he was to stop the first boy he met and take him to the Doges' Palace, where the Great Council, minus those of its members who were under thirty, was to be in full session, This boy, known as the *ballotino*, would have the duty of picking the slips of paper from the urn during the drawing of lots. By the first of such lots, the Council chose thirty of their own number. The second was used to reduce the thirty to nine, and the nine would then vote for forty, each of whom was to receive at least seven nominations. The forty would then be reduced, again by lot, to twelve, whose task was to vote for twenty-five, of whom each this time required nine votes. The twenty-five were in turn reduced to another nine; the nine voted for forty-five, with a minimum of seven votes each, and from these the *ballotino* picked out the names of eleven. The eleven now voted for forty-one – nine or more votes each – and it was these forty-one who were to elect the Doge.' From John Julius Norwich: *Venice. The Rise to Empire* (Allen Lane, London, 1977), p 190. And Europeans consider the election of a US president complicated?

[32] John Bagot Glubb (Sir John Glubb): *A Short History of the Arab Peoples* (Hodder and Stoughton, London, 1969), p 296

[33]   Arnold J Toynbee: *A Study of History vols I – VI* (abridged by D C Somervell; Oxford University Press, New York, 1946)

[34]   Charles Pasternak: *Quest. The Essence of Humanity* (John Wiley, Chichester, 2003), pp 368-370 and Charles Pasternak: Curiosity made us great, but it's waning in the West (*Times Higher Education Supplement* August 8, 2003)

[35]   Pygmy chimpanzees

[36]   Frans de Waal: *Our Inner Ape. The best and worst of human nature* (Granta Books, London, 2005), pp 136-137

[37]   See, for example, Jared Diamond in *Collapse: How Societies Choose to Fail or Survive* (Allen Lane, London, 2005), pp 107-111

[38]   The figures of those who died in Siberia are difficult to come by. According to the NKVD's own archives, a total of 18-20 million [Wikipedia], 40 million according to others [Colin Thubron: *In Siberia* (Penguin Books, London, 2000), p 10], were incarcerated at one time or another during Stalin's time: few made it out alive

[39]   In *Letter to the Burgomasters and Councillors of the Cities of Germany on behalf of Christian Schools* (1524), quoted by T L Jarman: ibid, p 147

[40]   Eric E Rich: *The Education Act 1870. A study of public opinion* (Longmans, London, 1970) p vii (foreword by Edward Boyle)

[41]   Gerard A Postiglione: The Opponents of Public Education: New York State, 1870-1880. *The Journal of Libertarian Studies* 6: numbers 3-4, 1982

[42]   Eric E Rich, ibid, p 26

[43]   Eric E Rich, ibid, p 11

[44]   See Matthew Chapman (a great-great-grandson of Charles Darwin): *40 Days and 40 Nights: Darwin, Intelligent Design, God, OxyContin and Other Oddities on Trial in Pennsylvania* (HarperCollins, 2007); Gordy Slack (son of a staunch fundamentalist): *The Battle Over the Meaning of*

Everything: Evolution, Intelligent Design and a School Board in Dover, PA (Jossey-Bass, 2007); Edward Humes: *Monkey Girl: Evolution, Education, Religion, and the Battle for America's Soul* (Ecco, 2007). For a complete account of the evidence submitted by a scientist on behalf of the parents at the trial, that encapsulates the essence of evolution, creationism and intelligent design, see http://www.sciohost.org/ncse/kvd/Padian/ Padian_transcript.html

[45] Karen Armstrong: *The Great Transformation: The World in the Time of Buddha, Socrates, Confucius and Jeremiah* (Atlantic Books, London, 2006), p 324

[46] See also David N Sedley: *Creationism and its Critics in Antiquity* (University of California Press, Berkeley, 2007)

[47] Marcus Tullius Cicero: *De Natura Deorum* (ed Andrew R Dyck, Cambridge U Press, Cambridge, 2003)

[48] Quoted by Francis Collins: *The Language of God. A Scientist Presents Evidence for Belief* (Simon & Schuster, London, 2007), p 230

[49] Ibid, p 158

[50] J H Tiner: *Isaac Newton: Inventor, Scientist and Teacher* (Mott Media, Milford, Michigan, 1975)

[51] Such as Dan Dennett [eg *Breaking the Spell: Religion as a Natural Phenomenon* (Viking Penguin, 2006)], Sam Harris [eg *Letter to a Christian Nation* (Knopf, 2006)], Richard Dawkins [eg *The God Delusion* (Black Swan, London, 2007)] or Christopher Hitchens [eg *God Is Not Great* (Hachette Book Group, 2007)]

[52] Bovine spongioform encephalitis, or 'mad cow' disease

[53] Quoted in John Adams: *Risk* (UCL Press, London, 1995), p 26

[54] That was in 1965; in 1973 it did join what has since become the European Union

CHAPTER 2

Major misconceptions and confusion: probability, risk and chance

Our improbable world

We spend our lives oscillating between the probable and the improbable. The formation of the world in which we live was one of the most improbable events ever to have occurred. There is general agreement nowadays among scientists that matter was created, around 14 billion years ago, by some kind of Big Bang. The matter, consisting first of hydrogen and then of helium, expanded into the galaxies and solar systems that exist today. Stars continue to produce helium at the huge temperatures (hundreds of millions of °C) within them by fusion: two hydrogen atoms [1] combine to form one helium atom, with a massive release of energy. At the UK Atomic Energy Authority in Culham, near Oxford, where I have my office, and at Cadarache in southern France, physicists are trying to mimic that reaction under controlled conditions (the hydrogen, or thermonuclear, bomb does it without restraint). If they are successful, fusion will become the most effective, environmentally-friendly, source of energy for the foreseeable future. To return to the Big Bang. 'If the rate of expansion one second after the Big Bang had been smaller by even one part in 100 thousand million million, the universe would have recollapsed before it ever reached its present size'. And 'if the rate of expansion had been greater by even one part in a million, stars and planets could not have been able to form. ... The existence of a universe as we know it rests upon a knife-edge of improbability' [2].

A similar improbability applies to the creation of the Earth, and the formation of elements like carbon, nitrogen, oxygen, phosphorus and sulphur, on which all life depends. 'If the strong nuclear force that holds together protons and neutrons had been even slightly weaker, then only hydrogen could have formed in the universe. If, on the other hand, the strong nuclear force had been slightly stronger, all the hydrogen would have been converted to helium, instead of the 25% that occurred early in the Big Bang, and thus the fusion furnaces of stars and their ability to generate heavier elements would never have been born... . Altogether there are fifteen physical constants whose value current theory is unable to predict. They are givens: they simply have the values that they have. The list includes the speed of light, the strength of the weak and strong nuclear forces, various parameters associated with electromagnetism, and the force of gravity. The chance that all of these constants would take on the values necessary to result in a stable universe capable of sustaining complex life forms is almost infinitesimal. ... In sum, our universe is wildly improbable' [2]. The two conclusions I have just mentioned have naturally generated much speculation and argument among physicists, philosophers and theists [3]

On the other hand, once having been formed from condensed gases spewed out by the sun, our planet behaves in a totally predictable way. Night follows day, and summer turns to autumn, with a constancy that our ancestors in Sumeria and Egypt, in China and Europe [4], in Central and South America, have been recording for thousands of years. The force of gravity remains constant, and we are as unlikely to float off the surface of the earth, as an aircraft without power is likely to stay there. (Except in the joke about an Irishman seated in a twin-engined Boeing 737, en route to Boston. Half way across the Atlantic the pilot comes on the intercom: 'Ladies and gentlemen, I have an announcement to make. Our starboard engine has failed. But there is absolutely no need to panic. The port engine is working well, and we are able to supply it with fuel from the starboard side of the plane. But because we have less thrust, I am afraid the journey will take a few hours longer. Sit back, and continue to enjoy the movie. The flight attendants will be bringing around complimentary drinks shortly.' 'Well I hope the other engine doesn't fail as well', the Irishman remarks to his neighbour, 'or we'll be up here for ever').

One of the fundamental features of the universe rests on an uncertainty. The continuous spectrum of light, from blue through purple to red, indicates that it travels in waves, like radio signals. Other observations show that it travels in the form of particles (termed photons), like the neutrons that are emitted when a radioactive source decays. It is impossible to describe light as only the one or the other. In the same way, an electron spinning round its atomic nucleus, has properties both of continuity and discreteness. In the early years of the twentieth century, Max Planck and Niels Bohr brought these dichotomies into a common theory that accounts for the movements of very small entities over very short distances: that of quantum mechanics. Planck applied quantum mechanics to photons, Bohr to electrons. The underlying feature of quantum mechanics was subsequently encapsulated by Werner Heisenberg in the uncertainty principle: it is not possible to measure simultaneously both the position and the momentum of such small particles [5].

If you have difficulty getting your head round quantum theory [6] and the uncertainty principle, don't worry. You're in very good company. Einstein didn't like it either, and argued about it with Max Born, a physicist who furthered the theory of quantum mechanics. 'You believe in a God who plays dice,' Einstein wrote to Born in 1944, 'and I in complete law and order in a world which objectively exists, and which I in a wildly speculative way, am trying to capture. ... Even the great initial success of the quantum theory does not make me believe in the fundamental dice game, although I am well aware that some of our younger colleagues interpret this as a consequence of senility. No doubt the day will come when we will see whose instinctive attitude was the correct one.' (It hasn't as yet). Physics, Einstein felt, 'should represent reality in time and space free from spooky actions at a distance.'

Born felt that Einstein's determinism runs counter to free will: just as probability underlies the behaviour of fundamental particles, so uncertainty in life is a prerequisite for responsibility and moral judgements. Einstein's philosophy, Born replied... 'somehow manages to harmonize the automata of lifeless objects with the existence of responsibility and conscience, something which I am unable to achieve' (that is, without the principle of uncertainty) [7]. There is indeed plenty of uncertainty left in the natural world.

Earthquakes and volcanoes

The earth's outer crust – whether at the bottom of the oceans or exposed in the form of land mass – sits, or rather floats, on the partially molten mantle (the part between the inner, molten core and the outer, solid crust) of the earth. The crust is divided into a number of separate segments, known as tectonic plates that are in constant motion. They slide past each other at speeds varying from a few millimetres to more than 10 centimetres per year. The Indian sub-continent, for example, is part of a tectonic plate that became detached from the earth's main landmass [8] some 167 million years ago. It gradually moved northwards until it collided with Eurasia 100 million years later. The collision caused the crust to buckle upwards, forming what is now the Himalayan mountain range. That is why there are sea shells high up in the mountains. The Himalayas continue to be squeezed upwards, gaining 20 millimetres in height every year.

When two tectonic plates become squeezed against each other at a particular point, the stress that is set up results in the propagation of seismic waves. These lead to earthquakes that, if generated under water, result in a tsunami. Earthquakes in the middle of a tectonic plate are rare and relatively innocuous. Earthquakes at the edges, or fault line, between two tectonic plates, are frequent and much more violent. The UK, situated within the Eurasian plate, experiences sizeable earthquakes (more than 5.8 on the Richter scale [9]) only every 100 years or so. It is an example of the first situation. The San Andreas fault in California, that runs 800 miles along the juncture between the Pacific and the North American plates (from Hollister in the north to the Salton Sea in the

Mohave desert in the south), is an example of the second situation: earthquakes measuring some 6.0 on the Richter scale occur every 20 years or so.

Molecular biologists may have mapped the sequence of all 3 billion letters of the human genome, astrophysicists may be able to tell us what happened within the first 10^{-43} of a second (a tenth of a millionth of a millionth of a millionth of a millionth of a millionth of a millionth of a millionth of a second) following the Big Bang, and astronomers may have been able to predict eclipses of sun and moon for more than two millennia, but geologists have been left behind. They are unable to foresee the next disaster with any accuracy whatever [10]. For example, early in 2004 scientists reported that there was a chance of an earthquake of around 6.6 on the Richter scale occurring later that year in southern California. It didn't happen, but then their prediction had been tempered by the qualification that the chance was only 50-50.

Measuring with considerable accuracy the 'slip rate' between the Pacific and the North American plates at the southern end of the San Andreas fault, which has not seen an earthquake like those at the centre (8.0 on the Richter scale in 1857) or northern end (7.9 on the Richter scale in 1906) over the past 250 years, enables Yuri Fialko to conclude no more than that the southern end, which comprises the densely populated areas of metropolitan Los Angeles, Orange County, San Diego and Tijuana (in Baja California) 'is probably in the late phase of interseismic recurrence' [11]. Put into simple language, Fialko says that 'The information available suggests that the fault is ready for the next big earthquake but exactly when the triggering will happen and where the earthquake will occur we cannot tell. It could be tomorrow or it could be 10 years or more from now' [12]. Not much help to home-owners in this area.

Occasionally adjacent tectonic plates move away from each other. When this happens there is a good chance of hot molten rock under extreme pressure escaping upwards, and being spewed out as lava and gases, such as sulphur dioxide and carbon dioxide, through the caldera, or opening, of a volcano [13]. Predicting activity from an existing volcano, by continuous monitoring of seismic activity near the caldera and by measuring sulphur dioxide emissions, is somewhat more accurate than predicting an earthquake. For example, while the *exact* timing and extent of the eruption of Mount St Helens in Washington State in 1980 was not established before the event, enough warning was given to enable 20,000 people at risk to be evacuated, though 57 fatalities did occur. A decade later, in the spring of 1991, US scientists were able to warn residents living near Mount Pinatubo in the Philippines, of an imminent eruption. By the time this happened a few months later, tens of thousand potential victims had been evacuated, though a thousand casualties (dead, injured, or missing) still resulted.

The plume of smoke was so extensive that global cooling, to the tune of $1°$ C, ensued [14]. Continuous monitoring of volcanoes around the world by satellite with a special type of radar, is likely to improve the predictability of volcanic eruptions significantly in the future. But not all types of volcano signal a possible eruption, through measurement of seismic unrest, well ahead of time. If the molten magma below a volcano is of the type known as rhyolite, it can ascend at the rate of a metre a second, or a transit time from 5 kilometres below ground to the surface in just 4 hours [15], as opposed to the more sluggish rise at most volcanoes that takes place over weeks or months. With rhyolite volcanoes, there is virtually no possibility of forewarning the public at all.

Courts of law

You may say that so long as those in positions of authority understand the nature of risk and probability, that's fine. The rest of us can lead our lives without worrying over the details. Not so if you're a member of a jury, though. Deciding on the innocence or guilt of the accused invariably requires an assessment of probability. What are the chances that the alleged thief was in the vicinity of the store when the bracelets were taken? – theft from private houses is barely ever investigated by the police these days: they just don't have the time – 100 to 1, even (50-50), or 1 to 100 against? In cases of alleged murder, it is particularly important for a jury to understand the rudiments of statistics. In the USA, the accused can land up in the electric chair. Actually no longer electric in most states: the condemned is given a lethal injection instead [16]. Let me give two examples, one from the USA and one from Britain.

Most people know the story. A famous footballer, O J Simpson, is indicted on a charge of murdering his ex-wife, Nicole Brown Simpson. DNA samples taken in the victim's house match those of the accused. The evidence seems irrefutable. Simpson will surely go down. Enter the defence team's adviser, Alan Dershowitz, professor of law at Harvard. The prosecution realised that the DNA evidence was shaky. Someone could have tampered with the samples. In any case, it was in the early days of forensic DNA technology, and the prosecution was not sure it could achieve a conviction on this evidence. Instead it switched to statements by witnesses who corroborated that Simpson had physically abused his wife on several occasions during their 18 years of marriage. 'A slap is a prelude to homicide', the prosecution contended. The defence had tried to keep such evidence out of court, but failed. On Dershowitz's advice, it turned to statistics.

'In 1992, according to the FBI Uniform Crime Reports, a total of 913 women were killed by their husbands, and 519 were killed by their boyfriends'.

Against this total of 1432 homicides, more than 2 and a ½ million women are battered annually by husbands or boyfriends. So the probability that an abuser goes on to murder is 1432 in 2 and a ½ million, or 1 in 2500. 'There is never any justification for domestic violence. But neither is there any scientifically accepted evidence that domestic abuse … is a prelude to murder.' Simpson was acquitted. Yet look at these figures more closely. As Gerd Gigerenzer, professor of psychology at the Max-Planck Institute for Adaptive Behaviour and Cognition in Berlin, points out [17], 'Dershowitz omitted one crucial piece of evidence from his calculation: that Nicole Brown Simpson had been murdered, not just battered. The relevant percentage is not how many men who slap or beat their domestic partners go on to murder them, as Dershowitz would have us believe. Instead, the relevant probability is that of a man murdering his domestic partner given that he battered her *and* that she was murdered.' Dershowitz's figure of 1 in 2,500 battered women being killed equates to 40 in 100,000. Gigerenzer goes on 'What we need in addition is the number of battered women who are killed each year by someone other than their partners … the *Uniform Crime Reports for the United States and Its Possessions* (1993) estimated (this to be) five women in 100,000.' The diagram constructed from this information is shown below (Fig 2.1), it may be concluded that 'the chances that a batterer actually murdered his partner given that she has been killed is about 8 in 9, or approximately 90%', not the 0.04% quoted by Dershowitz.

Fig 2.1: (Fig 8-1 of Gerd Gigerenzer *Reckoning with Risk. Learning to live with uncertainty* (Allen Lane: The Penguin Press, London, 2002), p 144.

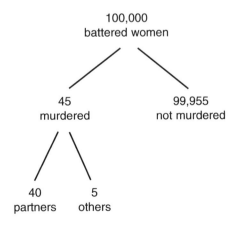

100,000
battered women

45
murdered

99,955
not murdered

40
partners

5
others

The next case I am going to describe involves an even smaller probability than the 1 in 2,500 used by Dershowitz: a probability of 1 in 73,000,000 that a certain event occurred. In this case it was used not by the defence to acquit an accused man, but by the prosecution to convict an accused woman. In 1997 Sally Clark, a solicitor from Cheshire, gave birth to a boy whom she and her husband named Christopher. At 11 weeks of age, Christopher died in his sleep. There was evidence of a respiratory infection, and the death was ascribed to natural causes. Fortunately the Clarks were able to have another child, and in 1998 a boy, Harry, was born. Eight weeks later disaster struck once more: little Harry was dead in his cot. Again it was likely that he had died from natural causes. But two cot deaths in a row? The police arrested the distraught couple, and the following year Sally Clark was charged with murder. First the prosecution alleged that both babies had been shaken to death. Three days into the trial certain members of the team changed their mind: the boys had been smothered. There was no forensic evidence to support either cause. An eminent paediatrician, Sir Roy Meadow, was called by the prosecution to testify.

Meadow had considerable experience of acting as an expert witness in earlier cases involving 'sudden infant death syndrome' (SIDS), or cot death. He had come to the conclusion that SIDS is often the result of child abuse by one the parents, brought on by what he termed 'Munchausen Syndrome by Proxy' (MSbP). Sufferers from this affliction deliberately harm a person in their care in order to gain the attention of medical personnel. Moreover Meadow was of the opinion that 'there is no evidence that cot deaths runs in families, but there is plenty of evidence that child abuse does' [18]. The chance of a cot death occurring in the population at large is 1 in 1303. But if the child is from an affluent, non-smoking family, with the mother over 26, the chance falls to around 1 in 8500 [19]. Meadow took the latter figure and argued that if the chance of a cot death in such a family (which corresponded to the Clarks' situation) is 1 in 8500, then the chance of two cot deaths is 1 in 8500 x 8500, or 1 in 72,250,000, which he 'rounded up' to 1 in 73 million. The jury, by a majority verdict of 10 to 2, found Sally Clark guilty of murder, and she was sentenced to life imprisonment.

An outcry soon erupted, as the fallacy of Meadow's calculation was exposed. An editorial in the *British Medical Journal* entitled 'Conviction by mathematical error? Doctors and lawyers should get probability theory right' appeared [20]. It pointed out that the squaring of the 1 in 8500 figure was unjustified. Since the first death had been accepted as a cot death, the probability of it having occurred was 1, not 1 in 8500. Second, Meadow's assumption that 'there is no evidence that cot deaths runs in families' was patently wrong: there are plenty of cases showing the opposite. Another article, 'Beyond reasonable doubt', written by Helen Joyce, the then-editor of a mathematical journal called *Plus* [21], went further. She refers to the following finding: the chance that the sibling of a child who has died from cot death will suffer the same fate, is between 10 to 22 times more likely than the average (the chance of an unrelated child dying from cot death). She then uses Bayesian theory – remember she's a mathematician – to calculate the probability that both of Sally Clark's sons died of natural causes, and comes out with a figure of 1 in 1.5 (not 1 in 73 million). In other words there's a 66% chance that Sally Clark was innocent of the charges laid against her.

In 2000 Sally Clark's lawers submitted an appeal to the High Court. It was rejected. It then transpired that one of the prosecution's witnesses had failed to disclose the results of tests that showed that one of the boys had died as a result of an infection with *Staphylococcus aureus*; he had not been smothered by his mother at all. A second appeal in 2003 was successful, and Sally was released from prison. She and her husband could at last return to a normal family life with their third son , born while Sally was in prison. It was not to be. The strain of the trial and its false accusations, the four years spent incarcerated, had surely taken their toll. Sally Clark died on 16 March 2007. She was just 42. Sir Roy Meadow was struck off the Medical Register by the British General Medical Council for 'serious professional misconduct' in 2005, having been involved, as expert witness, in the wrongful conviction of another mother for murder. He appealed to the High Court and won. At 74 years of age, he was free once more to enjoy his retirement.

Had the juries and the trial judges in these cases been better educated in the use of statistics, miscarriages of justice would have been prevented and several innocent people would not have gone to prison. 'Never again must mathematical error be allowed to conflict with mathematical fact as if each were a legitimate expert view', as a director of public health said in regard to the Sally Clark case [20].

There is talk in the UK of extending DNA testing to suspects accused of relatively minor offences, such as speeding or dropping litter in the street. One of Britain's most senior judges, Lord Justice Sedley, considers that putting *everyone* on a DNA database, irrespective of whether they have committed a crime or not, is fairer than restricting the database – at 4 million entries already the world's largest – to those accused of committing an offence. The current situation 'means that a great many people who are walking the streets, and whose DNA would show them guilty of crimes, go free' [22]. Quite how the sequence of As, Cs, Gs and Ts in a person's DNA shows them to be guilty of crimes, the good Lord does not say. If you are unlucky enough to find yourself in such a situation, take comfort from clever Gerd Gigerenzer once more [23]. Your DNA matches that found at the scene of the alleged offence. In court, an expert witness expresses his opinion: 'The probability that this match has occurred by chance is 1 in 100,000'. Your worst nightmare is at hand. But supposing the expert witness had put it somewhat differently: 'Out of every 100,000 people, I will show a match'. Since you live, say, in metropolitan London, Delhi or Beijing, each with a population exceeding 10 million, this means that there are more than a hundred people who would show a match. Feeling better already?

Road safety

What I am about to say will be considered by many to be thoughtless and dangerous. At best, politically incorrect. But in a chapter entitled 'Major misconceptions' I have to point out that the evidence regarding seat belts, drink driving, and speeding does not appear to bear out the claims made by transport departments throughout Europe.

'Available data for eight Western European countries which introduced a seat belt law between 1973 and 1976 suggest that it has not led to a detectable change in road deaths ... .' Indeed there is 'no foundation for the (UK) Department of Transport's oft-repeated claim that a seat belt law would save 1000 lives and 10,000 injuries a year' [24]. Presumably people with seat belts drive more recklessly than they used to without them, thus offsetting the undoubted efficacy of seat belts in an accident. The type of seat belt used, though, is important. Current 'across the chest' belts are undoubtedly more effective than 'lap seat belts'. In 1970 I was driving with my family across the USA, from La Jolla to the East Coast. Near the little town of Clinton, Missouri, we were involved in a head-on collision, caused by an oncoming reckless driver who was overtaking another car below the brow of a hill that we were approaching from the other direction and who therefore did not see our vehicle. We were all wearing lap seat belts (except my 3-year-old daughter: she was the only one unscathed). My wife suffered serious injury. At the moment of impact, the seat belt ruptured her intestine [25].

'Evidence for the effectiveness of countermeasures aimed at curbing drinking and driving is hard to find ... Scandinavia is often held up as an example of what can be achieved by draconian drink-drive legislation vigorously enforced. But ... in a report entitled "The Scandinavian myth" (it was) shown that the available data furnish no support for the legislative deterrence thesis. (An) interrupted-time-series analysis revealed no effect of the legislation on the relevant accident statistics' [26].

Recently the Department of Transport in the UK recommended reducing the speed limit in all urban areas from 30 mph to 20 mph (currently only parts of some towns have a 20 mph limit). The lower the speed limit, the fewer accidents: 'a third of all accidents are caused by speed', according to the Department. In fact just 5% of accidents are due to speeding. As for 20 mph versus 30 mph, the Department's own figures show that the rate of serious or fatal accidents in 30 mph zones is 13%; in the present 20 mph zones it is 17% [27].

Reducing road deaths – irrespective of the accuracy or not of the claims – is obviously to be encouraged. But whether politicians and bureaucrats understand probability or not, they are certainly blinkered by their preconceived ideas.

The BSE crisis and CJD

I referred in the previous chapter to the BSE outbreak that hit Britain in 1986. The agriculture minister of the day, John Gummer, tried to reassure an anxious public by telling it there was no risk to eating beef (he had his four-year-old daughter by his side, seemingly munching a beef burger). But there is a risk to everything we do. From riding a bicycle (a one in 75,000 chance of being killed), or going for a swim (a one in 20,000 chance of drowning), to driving a car (a one in 5300 chance of a fatal accident ending your life) [28]. Eating food is not immune from risk either: albeit generally of falling ill with an upset stomach, rather than death. Yet 5000 people in the USA die each year from food-borne diseases [29]. Over the two decades following the BSE outbreak, a total of 168 people [30] have so far died in Britain from variant Creutzfeldt-Jacob disease (vCJD), the human form of BSE. The numbers may be small, but CJD, in whatever form it comes, is a horrible, debilitating disease of the nervous system that generally ends in a painful and drawn-out death. As yet, there is no cure.

The link with BSE was by no means proven, merely suggestive. The likelihood was that CJD resulted from eating brain and blood-products from infected cattle. It was not an epidemic, though some scientists warned that it might become one. Fortunately it did not. Cattle themselves became infected (with BSE) when they were fed beef products, such as ground-up brain and other body parts, that are surplus to an abattoir, in order to try to fatten them up for market. One carcass that had developed BSE (by a route not yet clear) is likely to have been present among the others. Changing the diet of livestock from grass to one of their own kind does not make good farming. 'The story of BSE in Britain is a case study in the ruthless efficiency of intensive farming, the self-serving behaviour of government departments and the patronising caution extended to the public when explaining risk' [31]. It led to the slaughter of more than eight million cattle, and cost the British tax payer around £7 billion. It was 'the most expensive food scare the world has ever seen' [32]. Yet once a possible link to CJD was considered likely, there was little the government could do except to break it.

Scientists investigating BSE were reminded of a similar disease in sheep called scrapie. This is a neurological disease that is endemic in Britain and North America, but not, so far, in Australia or New Zealand [33]. The name derives from the observation that sick animals scrape themselves against a wall or a fence, irrespective of whether the latter is made of barbed wire or not. Presumably it is a violent itching of the skin felt by the animals that leads to this behaviour. The way that scrapie spreads through a herd is strongly suggestive of an infectious ailment. For years researchers had been trying to isolate the responsible microbe. It appeared to be neither a protozoan like that causing African sleeping sickness in cattle (*Trypanosoma brucei*), nor a bacterium like that responsible for bovine tuberculosis (*Mycobacterium tuberculosis*), nor a virus like that causing foot-and-mouth disease or bird influenza. In fact they couldn't find any DNA or RNA – the hallmarks of living things – in preparations that appeared to be infectious. All that these contained was some protein. Proteins can certainly be lethal. Look at what ricin did for unfortunate Georgy Markov [34], or the lethal effect of the neurotoxin in the saliva of the black mamba (*Dendroaspis polylepis*) [35]. But such toxins cannot reproduce themselves. Nor is there any known mechanism by which a protein can give rise to a self-replicating molecule like DNA or RNA.

The researchers were accused of sloppy science. Their purification methods were said to be inadequate. They'd obviously missed a bit of RNA or DNA. Undeterred, though finding it increasingly difficult to obtain grants for their research, they persevered. When preparations causing BSE were purified and analysed, these, too, appeared to consist of nothing but protein. Such proteins were termed 'prions' [36]. Calling molecules by fancy names does not convince a sceptic any more than calling someone a miracle worker, or referring to a medicament as a wonder drug: you have to prove the point. And in the end they did. The pieces started to fit together, like a jigsaw puzzle, which is very much the way scientific enquiry proceeds. It became clear that CJD, like BSE and scrapie, is a disease transmitted by prions. Highly purified prion preparations (free of any traces of nucleic acid) from a sheep with scrapie, or a human with CJD, were injected into the brains of mice. Months later the recipient animals developed the typical neurological symptoms of scrapie or CJD. Although the exact mechanism by which prion proteins cause disease is still not clear, a totally new mode of infection had been discovered. Stanley Prusiner, the leading scientist involved in this study, was awarded a Nobel prize in 1997 [37]. It is the unexpected in science that makes it such a rewarding discipline.

Fig 2.2: Decline of BSE and Kuru [reproduced from *Les Prix Nobel 1997* (Nobel Foundation, Stockholm, 1998) p 296, with permission].

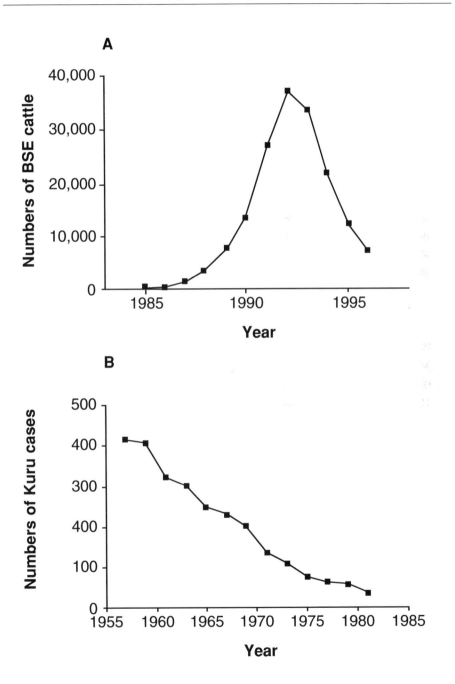

None of this was known in the late 1980s when the BSE crisis erupted. But a link between the consumption of certain types of meat and CJD already seemed likely, because of a totally unrelated sequence of events. Kuru is a disease among the Fore people of Papua New Guinea. Its symptoms are similar to those of CJD, and the outcome, too, is generally fatal. Women and children are the main victims. During the 1960s, Carleton Gajdusek was investigating how kuru is transmitted. He came to the conclusion that cannibalism, which was practised by the Fore, had something to do with it. These people eat the meat of dead relatives as part of their ritualistic mourning ceremony: women and children are the main participants. The more cases Gajdusek examined, the better the correlation became. Eating human flesh leads to kuru. Gajdusek persuaded the Fore to desist from their rites. Once they did so, the incidence of kuru declined [Fig 2.2]. Gajdusek understood the nature of probability well enough. His work earned him a Nobel prize in 1976, two decades before Prusiner's.

The minister for agriculture in 1990 was not a scientist (though his advisers were). Nor did he understand the nature of risk. At best, if he was unsure of the precise statistics, he should have said was that 'eating beef poses no *significant* risk to health', or that 'eating beef poses an *insignificant* risk to health'. But then he was a politician, whose duty it was to defend the farming business. The latter statement would have frightened off millions of potential beef eaters, because the public doesn't understand risk either.

To turn to the risk of contracting, or suffering from, other potentially fatal diseases. Even scientifically-enlightened members of the public are likely to misconstrue risk when expressed in terms of probabilities. Take a typical example. 'The probability that a woman of 40 has breast cancer is about 1%. If she has breast cancer, the probability that she tests positive on a screening mammogram is 90%. If she does not have breast cancer, the probability that she nevertheless tests positive is 9%' [38]. Reading the above, any woman of 40 who has just tested positive with a mammogram, is likely to assume that the probability of her having breast cancer is 90%. Instead of the tears, and fright, and stress, that this statistic causes, she would be well advised to follow the analysis of risk not in terms of probabilities, but in the form of 'natural frequencies'.

Gerd Gigerenzer expresses the above probabilities as follows. 'Think of 100 women. One has breast cancer, and she will probably test positive. Of the 99 who do not have breast cancer, 9 will also test positive. Thus, a total of 10 women will test positive.' Of those 10, only one will actually have breast cancer. In other words, the chance of her having breast cancer is not 90%, but 10%. Please don't think that Gigerenzer or I recommend ignoring a positive mammogram. But equally, until the cancer is confirmed by further tests, there is no need to think the worst just yet.

The human genome has been sequenced. Can we now expect to visit a doctor's surgery, or perhaps purchase a home kit, to tell us which diseases we are likely to contract over our lifetime? Not a bit of it. First, of course, because many diseases don't directly involve our genes at all. Infections caused by viruses, bacteria and protozoa are the prime examples. Most are benign, but others can be deadly. In the next chapter, I will discuss human immunodeficiency virus (HIV). Other viruses, like Ebola or Lassa fever, are as bad, but you're unlikely to be struck down by these if you live in the temperate climate of North America, Europe or Asia. You are much more likely to become infected with the common cold virus, or with measles, mumps or rubella (German measles) virus, or with a rotavirus that gives you severe diarrhoea. Vaccination against the trio of measles, mumps and rubella (MMR) is effective; the risk of vaccination itself eliciting disease is discussed in the following chapter. Rarely are any of these infections fatal. The same is true of most infections caused by bacteria. In fact the trillions of *Escherichia coli* that inhabit our gut are actually beneficial, because they prevent pathogenic relatives from taking hold. But very occasionally a lethal strain of *E coli* such as 0157 does emerge, generally from contaminated meat. The outcome can be fatal. Much more common are minor intestinal upsets due to *Salmonella*, a topic to which I return briefly in Chapter 6. Note that we harbour on average more than 160 different species of bacteria in our gut [39]. So far as protozoa are concerned, it is the traveller to tropical and sub-tropical zones who needs to worry about malaria or leishmaniasis. Well, not only the traveller.

The billion people who live on less than a dollar a day, predominantly in southern Asia and sub-Saharan Africa, are subject to every form of infection – often simply for lack of clean water [40] – that hits them. Being malnourished, their immune system simply can't cope, and over 3 million die annually from malaria, HIV, measles and tuberculosis (10 million more die simply from hunger-related causes). All these diseases are in principle preventable [41]. The ranting of pop stars and the billions of dollars poured into the pockets of venal politicians by governments and the World Bank have done little to improve the situation over more than a decade (the Bank itself admits that 30% of its aid is lost due to corruption; the figure is probably much higher).

Notice that earlier I used the word 'directly' in relation to genes. This is because we know that a certain genetic make-up can help to protect against particular infectious diseases. Some people, for example, lack the receptor for HIV on the surface of their lymphocytes, and therefore do not become infected.

Others have an abnormal type of haemoglobin in their red blood cells, which prevents the malarial parasite [42] from reproducing.

Then there are nutritional diseases. Malnutrition among the 5 million children who die every year because they don't even have a small bowl of rice a day on account of their parents' poverty, has little to do with genetic make-up. Nor does the guzzling of food and sweet drinks by the 25% or more of Westerners who are clinically obese [43]. In the latter case, however, there is a ray of hope. For research is showing that appetite has a genetic background [44]. If you happen to possess an appetite-promoting gene, it may in the future be possible to take medication to suppress its activity [45].

The second reason why detailed analysis of one's genetic make-up is not going to provide an accurate prognosis of future ailments, is that most diseases do not depend on a single gene. Monogenetic diseases like cystic fibrosis (CF) or severe immunodeficiency disease (SCID) are the exception. They are rare, because sufferers tend to die before child-bearing age, so the rogue gene gradually becomes eliminated from a population. But not entirely. This is because those who have inherited the faulty gene from only one parent [46] don't have overt symptoms. The faulty gene is therefore passed on from generation to generation. Another reason for the retention of faulty genes within a population is that in heterozygotes it may actually be of benefit in certain situations. The faulty haemoglobin mentioned in connection with malaria is a case in point.

Common diseases like heart failure, cancer, stroke, or diabetes depend on a subtle interplay between a whole range of different genes, most as yet unrecognised, as well as on environmental factors like diet, an infectious episode, exposure to toxic chemicals or plain stress. So there is a long way to go before a read-out of your DNA can predict your future health. And even if you do know, for example, that you carry a *BRCA* gene that raises the likelihood of contracting breast cancer by 30-40%, what are you going to do about it? By constant monitoring for tiny lumps you may be able to diagnose the cancer early enough to halt, and reverse, its growth successfully. But you may also worry yourself sick, and constant stress is itself a risk factor for developing cancer. In the future, scientists will no doubt find ways of suppressing genetic risk factors such as a *BRCA* gene. To try to predict when this will happen is not at all easy, despite enthusiastic scenarios [47]. The gene that gives rise to cystic fibrosis was discovered several decades ago. Since then scientists have tried to cure sufferers by administering the correct version through relatively straightforward procedures. None has so far been successful.

When the sequencing of the human genome project was announced a decade ago President Bill Clinton prophesied that 'With this profound new knowledge, humankind is on the verge of gaining immense, new power to heal. It will revolutionize the diagnosis, prevention and treatment of most, if not all, human diseases.' The knowledge has given an enormous spurt to basic science, but it has so far been of little benefit to human health. The situation is reminiscent of President Nixon's forecast in the early 1970s that cancer would soon be on the way out. His erstwhile opponent John F Kennedy had been responsible for putting a man on the moon: he, Richard Milhous Nixon, would cure cancer. Aware that viruses were being implicated in the emergence of certain malignant tumours, he greatly increased financial support for this kind of research. Insight into the biology of viruses in terms of cellular RNA and DNA burgeoned, and Nobel prizes dropped out of the sky on to grateful researchers. But 10, 20 years on, the number of people dying from cancer had hardly changed. The predictability of advances in medicine is no better than the forecast of earthquakes and volcanoes.

The millennium bug, or Y2K

I referred in the previous chapter to the way A J Ayer differentiates the three ways in which we use the word 'chance'. The chance of the universe coming into being, of the earth continuing its 24-hour cycle of spinning around itself, of scientists being able to predict the exact position of fundamental particles, are examples of *judgements of a priori probability*: infinitesimally small in the first case, infinitesimally large in the second, and infinitesimally small in the third. The chance of a crime suspect being guilty, the chance of contracting vCJD from eating BSE-infected meat, the chance of having breast cancer, and the chance of contracting various diseases based on analysis of our DNA, are *estimates of actual frequency*. The third category recognised by Ayer is one based on *judgements of credibility*. The rest of this chapter will give instances of such appraisals. Before a statistician points out to me that fundamentally the three categories are not really so different, and that there is in any case some overlap, let me at once agree. I have used them merely to break up this chapter into convenient parts.

Towards the end of the last century, people started worrying about what would happen at midnight on 31 December 1999. I don't mean anything like the end of the world, though Nostradamus's predictions in that regard were once more brought to our attention by the more fanciful feature writers. I refer to the behaviour of computers. By 1999, computers were not just being used to classify scientific information, to write letters, or to access email. They were an intrinsic part of military defence systems, of air traffic control centres, of hospital management and power stations, of the supply of water, gas and electricity, of ambulance, police and fire brigade operations, of the banking system, of supermarkets … All such computers contain a date (and time). For simplicity, most computers had only two figures allotted to the year: 75 in 1975, 86 in 1986, and so on. By 1997 it had begun to dawn on those concerned that as 99 turned to 00, the system might break down (even if the entire year was shown, it wasn't obvious that 1999 would click smoothly to 2000; it might revert to 1900 instead).

'I'm one of the culprits who created this problem. I used to write those programs back in the 1960s and 1970s, and was proud of the fact that I was able to squeeze a few elements of space out of my program by not having to put a 19 before the year. Back then, it was very important. We used to spend a lot of time running through various mathematical exercises before we started to write our programs so that they could be very clearly delimited with respect to space and the use of capacity. It never entered our minds that those programs would have lasted for more than a few years. As a consequence, they are very poorly documented. If I were to go back and look at some of the programs I wrote 30 years ago, I would have one terribly difficult time working my way through step-by-step.' Who do you think said that? One of Bill Gates's chief nerds? It was actually Alan Greenspan, by now Chairman of the Federal Reserve, testifying before the Senate Banking Committee in February of 1998.

No one was sure what would happen. The commercial market saw an opportunity to cash in. Software companies sold kits that would avoid computer glitches on the day, and car makers Kia put out a commercial saying that Y2K meant 'Yes to Kia'. One speaker at a Stanford University conference in April 1998 predicted that the cost of fixing the problem in the USA might be 'greater than the entire cost of the Vietnam War', while another calculated that measures to prevent disasters throughout the world would amount to 'between $600 billion and $1.6 trillion globally' [48]. In the event, probably more than $300 billion was spent on contingency measures. Stories of possible disaster circulated in the press, novels with titles like *Deadline Y2K* appeared, a game called *Systems Failure* (in which aliens exploit global energy breakdown to invade the Earth) sold well, a song entitled *Crash* hit the charts, Catherine Zeta-Jones and Sean Connery played thieves who capitalise on the Y2K disaster in a film called *Entrapment*, and the millenium bug came top of Sky One's *50 Terrible Predictions*.

People began to change their Christmas holiday plans. My sister is an intelligent person, but easily worried by newspaper articles of impending doom. She and my brother-in-law were in the habit of going down to their house in Almeria province, in south-eastern Spain, for a few weeks over the holiday period. She began to fret that flying was no longer safe. 'But you're going down before Christmas, and not returning until well into January', I pointed out, hoping they'd invite me down. Next she turned to the possibility that the electricity supply would fail, once they were in Spain. Actually this happens all the time. The location of their house, deep in the countryside, suffers stoppages at every clap of thunder. 'If you're going to be without electricity, you're better off in Spain, where it's considerably warmer than in Northamptonshire. Also there you have butano heaters, here you're dependent on electricity for heat', I countered. Scientist brothers can be infuriating. Like thousands of others, however, the Ramsays didn't travel that year.

It was a situation where no one was prepared to speculate on the chances of a catastrophe striking the civilised world; the under-developed countries of Asia, Africa and Latin America were, of course, immune to all this. The US Deputy Secretary of Defense warned that 'The Y2K problem is the electronic equivalent of the El Ni–o and there will be nasty surprises around the globe.' So what actually happened? Very little. It is true that in Japan, some radiation-monitoring equipment failed (temporarily) at midnight, a nuclear power station sounded an alarm at two minutes past midnight, errors in data management by a telecommunications company appeared (the problem was fixed within three hours), and some mobile telephones lost incoming messages on the first of January. In Australia, bus-ticket-validation machines failed in two states, in the USA 150 slot machines at race tracks in Delaware stopped working, and French TV had to apologise for the fact that their weather forecast on the first of January showed the date as 01/01/19100. Apart from other minor glitches, nothing. As the Australian media put it, 'Computing consultants laughing all the way to the bank'.

But the huge sums spent on providing fail-safe mechanisms were justified 21 months later. As terrorists flew hijacked planes into buildings in Washington, DC and New York City, and into the ground in Pennsylvania, on 11 September, 2001, all flying aircraft were quickly grounded by measures that had been put in place two years earlier. The global banking system that operates out of the financial district of New York did not break down as the Twin Towers collapsed, because back-up data at multiple sites had been installed in readiness for Y2K. Two years later, in August 2003, when the electricity supply in the north-east of the USA failed, power was quickly restored because new equipment and systems had been set up in 1999. The appropriately-named Long Now Foundation in the USA is already prepared for the next blip, which will occur in eight thousand years, when the year 9999 turns to 10,000: the date on its computers is already given in five digits (so at the time of writing they are showing 02011) [49].

Astrology, ESP and homeopathy
I have lumped these three topics together for a simple reason: the probability that any of them works is virtually nil.

Astrology, which is more than 4000 years old, encompasses two tenets. The first is that celestial bodies influence events on Earth, a proposition that links it to ancient religions. It is true that extraterrestrial bodies within our solar system affect the physical state on Earth. The relationship between Sun and Earth accounts for the changes of season, and periodic sun-spots or flares cause episodes of global warming. The position of the moon affects the extent of ocean tides through gravitational forces. But the ancients knew none of this. Until the seventeenth century astrology and astronomy were indistinguishable. Then astronomy became a science based on experimental evidence, astrology a system of beliefs. By 1870 Gustave Flaubert could confidently say: 'Astronomy: a fine science. Useful only to sailors. While on the subject, laugh at astrology' [50]. In the same way chemistry parted from alchemy a century later (Isaac Newton still dabbled extensively in alchemy).

The second proposition, which is the crux of today's astrology, is that the position of Sun, Moon, planets and other stars relative to each other at the precise time of our birth has a bearing on how our lives will pan out. Pythagoras was one of the first to question this by drawing attention to the fact that the world does not affect identical twins in the same way [51]. Also, why should someone born on a particular day in one year, have the same horoscope as someone born on that day in another year? The answer provided by Elizabeth Teisser in *Your Horoscope* for 1993 is that the Earth ends up in the same place in the sky on the same date each year. This is nonsense. Because Earth is not a perfect sphere, but flatter at the poles and wider at the equator, it spins and wobbles, like a top, as it progresses around the Sun [52]. As a result it finishes up in a different position relative to the Sun – never mind relative to the other celestial bodies that are supposed to determine our horoscope – by some 22 thousand miles in successive years [53]. So allocating a particular sign of the zodiac – Pisces, say, to someone born on 7 March – is totally arbitrary. If that person's future were indeed to depend on some complex spatial relation between Earth, Sun and the other celestial bodies, one would have to specify the year of birth, and produce a separate zodiac for every year.

Yet astrology is as popular as ever. I referred in the previous chapter to the 52% of Europeans who consider astrology to be 'rather scientific' [54]; 60% of Britains regularly consult their horoscope, and this is said to include a third of all science students [55]; 48% of investors on the NY stock exchange use horoscopes to decide on when and what to buy or sell [56]. Newspapers, magazines, TV stations and the internet ('Enhance your relationships, manifest a satisfying career and more with these personalized readings! Click here') rely heavily on horoscopes to sell their wares. It's really big business.

A study recently published confirms that all this is pure claptrap. The survey, begun in London in 1953, tracked the lives of 2000 people who were born within minutes of each other. A hundred different characteristics, that astrologers claim can be predicted from birth charts, were assessed. These included occupation, anxiety levels, marital status, aggressiveness, sociability, IQ levels, ability in art, sport, mathematics and reading. No evidence of any similarities whatsoever between these 2000 'time twins' was found. The authors stated that 'The test conditions could hardly have been more conducive to success ... but the results are uniformly negative' [55].

Before I leave this topic, I need to come clean: there is evidence that people's birth date *can* influence their subsequent lives. Gabriele Doblhammer is an Austrian scientist who noticed something very surprising. She was studying the life expectancy of Austrians and Danes who had been born between 1863 and 1918. Those whose birth date fell between October and December lived – on average – longer than those born between April and June. The reason for this is not obvious, but seems to depend on their nutritional status *in utero* (in other words, the mother's nutritional status) and in infancy. It is known that heavy babies generally have longer life spans than lean ones, but why the Austrian and Danish families ate better during the late autumn than during the early summer is not clear. Before you tell me that this confirms a difference between those born under the sign of Libra, Scorpio or Sagittarius (roughly October to December) and those born under Aries, Taurus or Gemini (roughly April to June), I have to reveal another outcome of Gabriele Doblhammer's research. She studied the records of Australians born around the same time (late nineteenth century and early twentieth century). Here too there was a difference between those born between October and December, and those born between April and June, but the outcome was the exact opposite: the April to June cohorts lived longer than the October to December ones. Immigrants who had been born in England, showed the same pattern as those born in Austria or Denmark. This clearly shows that the *season* in which these people were born, not their astrological sign of the zodiac, determines their longevity. As more recent cohorts of Austrians, Danes and Australians were studied, the differences in longevity became progressively weaker, again showing that the effect had to do with environmental conditions in the late nineteenth and early twentieth century, not with the signs of the zodiac [57].

Other studies have looked at the predisposition of babies to develop multiple sclerosis (MS) later on in life. Scotland is a good place to study this, as the Scots have the highest incidence of MS in the world. It was found that those born in late spring (March, April, May and June) show a higher incidence of MS than those born during the autumn and winter months (September to January).

The conclusion that was drawn [58] is that foetal development in the womb of mothers exposed to levels of sunlight somehow increases the chances of their offspring developing MS. I should say that the exact cause of MS is not clear. It has, however, been known for a long time that both environmental and genetic factors are involved. This, as mentioned above, is of course true of most diseases. In the case of MS (and other diseases that result from an autoimmune cause), the environmental component has been attributed to a possible virus infection. Lack of sunlight in pregnant mothers appears now to be another component (the two may of course be related). As with longevity, the zodiacal sign plays no role. People living in southern climes are known to be less susceptible to MS than their northern counterparts. Even more to the point is that an earlier study in Canada had come to the same conclusion as the more persuasive Scottish one, except that the times of most and least risk were shifted by about a month.

ESP

ESP (extra sensory perception) received a boost during the 1920s, when Joseph Banks Rhine, chairman of the Psychology Department at Duke University in the USA, carried out a series of experiments that seemed to prove the existence of telepathy. He used professional mediums, in cities hundreds of miles away, to tell him what card he was holding in his hand at any one time. Instead of playing cards he used 'Zener cards' [59], that would make the chances of coming up with the right answer 1 in 5, or 20%. The results were startling. Time and again the number of correct answers exceeded the expected probability. Many years later, studies with such cards were repeated – several thousand times – by a scientist called David Langmuir. This time the overall distribution of correct answers was exactly as anticipated. Telepathy was bunkum after all. Unfortunately Langmuir did not publish his results, nor did he challenge Rhine with them. But he told his uncle, Irving Langmuir, a Nobel Laureate in chemistry, about them. Irving senior himself approached Rhine, only to discover that the 'father of parapsychology' had deliberately concealed hundreds of thousands of negative answers [60].

Conjurors [61] and mediums, however, continue to amaze us with their seemingly extraordinary powers of ESP. Perhaps there is some unknown physical force at work after all? No. You yourself can surprise a group of friends at a dinner party by reluctantly admitting that you have the 'gift of telepathy'. In order to show you how it's done, I quote verbatim from the book to which I have just referred [62]:

'After such an opening, it is certain that someone there will beg you to tell more about it and will insist on a demonstration to prove your claim. You then explain that, for this telepathy to occur, there must be two brains on the same wavelength and that you discovered such a neural concordance with a colleague after several experiences. This colleague, who is with his family right now a few miles away is (say) Mr Norris (you name him explicitly). You are able to concentrate on a playing card and, just by thinking about it, you can tell Mr Norris which card it is. This works pretty often, not always, but pretty often. (It is important to be hesitant and to be restrained in your claim, short of 100% effectiveness.)

'Then you yield to the friendly pressure to make an attempt then and there. "Okay, I'll try," you say, "but I can't guarantee anything. I'll have to call my colleague, and I don't even know if he's there. I think his phone number is ...". After giving it you ask, "Do you people have a deck of cards?" Someone brings you a deck. You don't touch it, you ask someone else to shuffle it and have it cut again and again, and then you have the other people present to decide among themselves who will draw the card at random. Finally a card is drawn – the seven of clubs, for example.

'Before getting ready and concentrating on the card, you take out an address book to double-check the telephone number, and you jot it down together with your colleague's name on a piece of paper. You give this to the person who's been chosen to make the phone call. The call will be made from a different room from the one you'll be in when you are mentally transmitting the image of the card, the seven of clubs, over a distance to your colleague.

'The card is placed in front of you, and holding your head in your hands, you focus on it while taking deep breaths. Seconds, then minutes slowly pass. The people there have you in their sight the entire time. Ten minutes later, the person who made the call returns with undisguised astonishment: unbelievable though it may seem, Mr Norris said – after much hesitating and receiving of hazy visions – that he perceived a seven of clubs! You are totally spent and out of breath. You hold your head saying "Whew! That's really exhausting. I won't do that again for a really long time. It's really hard and I think my brain is overheated".

'All doubts melt away, quickly transformed into testimonials. "It's amazing! The cards were handled only by us. You told us his name in advance, and his phone number, too. It's not your house, so the room can't have been set up to trick us somehow – no hidden transmitter."

'The person who made the phone call swears that the person who answered didn't squeeze information out of him. The caller simply asked for the appropriate person, explaining why, and gave no information of any kind that would have given any indication of the card chosen.

'What happened was truly extraordinary. One or two people may still harbour some doubt but lack the power to make a reasoned argument ...

'Before we leave the scene, let's look at your address book, at the page for last names starting with N (like your colleague's). Here's what we see:

Alexander	Ace of hearts
Andrew	Two of hearts
Anthony	Three of hearts

etc, etc, through diamonds, clubs (Mark = Seven of clubs) and spades, including a name for the joker.

'This sheds a bright light on your telepathic gifts ... You never state the first name until the card is drawn. It is written down after consultation of the address book. The sole purpose of this consultation is to avoid your having to memorize fifty-three (... one of the authors, having been caught out by his own brother during one of these long-distance-telepathy demonstrations, thought it prudent to add a name to correspond to the joker – the card chosen on purpose by that wily brother).

'After you apparently verified the phone number, you write the number on a piece of paper, together with the name, including the first name chosen from the list – in this case, Mark. This is the piece of paper you give to the person making the call.

'The number of people with all the pieces of information needed to figure out the mystery is reduced virtually to one. The person phoning rarely thinks to tell others that, in addition to information already given, the first name of the colleague has now been provided. ... And you can discount another worry. Your friend Mr Norris has his copy of the list of first names next to his phone and doesn't have to rack his brain to guarantee a high-quality psychic performance. All he has to do is to hesitate a little before giving, slowly, the name of the card.

'Possible variants of the scenario have been foreseen. For example: "Hello, may I speak to Mr Norris, please?" [Oh no, they didn't give me his first name!]

"Whom do you want? There are several brothers here."

"Uh, the one who practises telepathy, we're doing an experiment." [Still no first name].

"Well, in this family we all do telepathy a little bit."

"I was looking for Mark Norris." [Got it!]

"Speaking."

'Nothing could be simpler, as you can see. We recommend including the real first name of your colleague in your list, in case a lucky break gets you the particular card corresponding to his actual first name. Then you *really* have a complete triumph. You can then say "Check the phone number yourself in the phone book," which will supply your friends with the first name without any intervention on your part...'

Homeopathy

The word homeopathy [63] owes much to Samuel Hahnemann (1755-1843), a physician who proposed that taking a small amount of something that might have caused you to become ill in the first place, will actually make you better. This is akin to the way vaccination works. A small amount of a virus, bacterium, or protozoan, that would cause severe symptoms if large amounts entered the system, is deliberately introduced into the body. The outcome of the small amount is to render the person immune to a larger amount subsequently ingested, inhaled or absorbed through a lesion in the skin. In the following chapter, vaccination is described in greater detail. Vaccinating against smallpox, polio, diphtheria, tetanus, typhoid, measles and countless other pathogenic microbes, has probably saved more lives than all other medical treatments combined. It makes this form of homeopathy the success story of modern medicine. But, as with astrology, that is not what believers in this discipline have in mind.

Many homeopathic remedies are similar to the health foods discussed in the next chapter. Ever since Hahnemann's time, a central feature of homeopathic treatment has been the concept of infinite dilution. The remedy is diluted so much that an average dose contains less than a single molecule of it. In other words, it is pure water to which some sugar is added 'to make it palatable'. Nevertheless homeopathy has a huge following. Homeopathic products are widely advertised, and sell well. It's big business: sales in the USA reached $1.5 billion in 2000 [64]. You can take homeopathic courses on the internet. There are Institutes of Homeopathy throughout the world. In the UK there is a Homeopathy Research Institute that is linked to the University of Sheffield, and in the USA, the original Hahnemann College of Homeopathy is now part of Drexel University College of Medicine in Philadelphia. Even sane politicians are taken in [65]. It took a nineteenth century cleric to put it into perspective:

> Stir the mixture well
> Lest it prove inferior,
> Then put half a drop
> Into Lake Superior.
> Every other day
> Take a drop in water,
> You'll be better soon
> Or at least you oughter [66]

Those of us who, like the perceptive bishop, are not blinkered by ridiculous homeopathic claims, recognise that if someone's condition improves as a result of ingesting a worthless medicament, it reflects no more than the 'placebo' effect (see Chapter 5). That's not how adherents of homeopathy see it, of course. When challenged with the fact that a dose is devoid of the intended remedy, they reply that the water with which it has been diluted somehow 'remembers' the original presence of the beneficial molecules.

Some years ago, at biophysical meetings I used to attend, there was talk of 'structured' water. The properties of such water were proposed to be different from those of water in its liquid form. We know that frozen water – ice crystals – assumes a structure unlike that of liquid water. Water at an interface, or near some other boundary, might be different too. Since biophysicists are interested in living matter, we decided to test whether the water inside a biological cell, that is crammed full of proteins, lipid membranes and so forth, is different to water in a jar. As a criterion, we determined the ability of a small molecule like ATP (see Chapter 1) to rotate freely; nuclear magnetic resonance spectroscopy was used as a probe. The answer was clear: ATP is as free to rotate inside a living cell as it is in pure water. Perhaps, then, the 'memory' that water has of a homeopathic remedy with which it has been in contact is not simply one of 'structure'. Something else may be involved.

In June 1988 a *bona fide* scientist – an immunologist called Jacques Benveniste who was head of INSERM [67] Unit 200 in Paris – published a paper [68] in the respected journal *Nature*, which claimed to show 'memory' in water. There was an outcry among the scientific community. How could the editor have allowed such nonsense to be printed? John Maddox, the editor at the time, decided to make amends by visiting Benveniste's laboratory and watching the scientist's assistant, one Elisabeth Davenas, go through the experiment. For good measure, Maddox took along a magician, to spot potential trickery. None was found, and the initial results corroborated Benveniste's claims. Maddox then asked Davenas to repeat the experiment one more time in a 'blind' manner, so that she did not know which tubes she was analysing: they were coded by the *Nature* team and handed to her for analysis. This time there was no difference between plain water and the homeopathically diluted sample [69]. Benveniste's team continued their claims for a few years, but then the evidence for 'memory' in water simply fizzled out. To paraphrase *Matthew 22:14*: Many claims are made, but few are sustained. The homeopathic 'law of infinitesimals' is a figment of the imagination.

So the formation of the world we inhabit was a most improbable event. Other circumstances are more probable, yet not clear-cut: the predictability of earthquakes and volcanic eruptions, the guilt of a supposed murderer, the reason for a car crash, the transmission of 'mad cow disease' to humans, the possibility of systems failure as 1999 became 2000. Scientists are working hard on the first, but the judiciary and juries don't understand probability well enough to pass sound judgements, governments and their advisors don't understand (or wish to understand) the risks involved in driving a car or eating beef, and everyone was deluded by the possibility of catastrophic consequences as the clocks struck midnight on 31 December 1999. We all need to remind ourselves of simple probability theory. We also need to avoid jumping to premature conclusions. The sequencing of the human genome in 2001 was a scientific tour de force, but predicting one's future illnesses is still a long way off. Many people believe in astrology, ESP and homeopathy. To them I offer only this remark of Einstein's: 'Two things are infinite, the universe and human stupidity. But I'm not so sure about the universe' [70].

Notes

[1]   Actually 1 deuterium, a stable, heavy isotope of hydrogen, plus 1 tritium, a radioactive, even heavier isotope of hydrogen

[2]   Stephen Hawking in *A Brief History of Time*, quoted by Francis Collins: *The Language of God. A Scientist Presents Evidence for Belief* (Simon & Schuster, London, 2007), p 73

[3]   For a synopsis of current views, see Paul Davies: *The Goldilocks Enigma. Why is the universe just right for life?* (Allen Lane, London, 2006). Note also Roger Penrose: *Cycles of Time: An Extraordinary New View of the Universe* (Bodley Head, 2010)

[4]   I am thinking of the stone circles of Stonehenge and others elsewhere

[5]   Currently quantum considerations are being applied not just to elementary particles, but to entities as large as molecules. See, for example, JR Minkel: The *Gedanken* Experimenter, *Scientific American* 297, Aug 2007, pp 78-79 and Philip Ball: Quantum all the way, *Nature* 453: 22-25, 2008. The fact that a single photon can be in several places at once has recently been demonstrated: see Vladan Vuletic: Entangled quartet. *Nature* 468: 384-385, 2010

[6]   Try Jim Baggott: *The Quantum Story: A History in 40 Moments* (Oxford University Press, 2011)

[7]   From Born, M: *The Born-Einstein letters* (Macmillan, London, 1971), quoted by John Adams: *Risk* (UCL Press, London, 1995), p 17; see also

Manjit Kumar: *Quantum: Einstein, Bohr and the Great Debate About the Nature of Reality* (Icon Books, Thriplow, 2008) and Roger G Newton: *Einstein was Correct, but Bohr Won the Game* (World Scientific, Singapore/ Imperial College Press, London, 2009)

[8] Gondwana: present-day Antarctica, Africa, South America and Australasia

[9] An exponential, ie logarithmic, scale that expresses the local seismic energy released

[10] See, for example, Susan E Hough: *Predicting the Unpredictable: The Tumultuous Science of Earthquakes* (Princeton U Press, 2009), reviewed in *Nature* 463: 735, 2010 and Florin Diacu: *Megadisasters: The Science of Predicting the Next Catastrophe* (Princeton U Press/Oxford U Press, 2009)

[11] Yuri Fialko: Interseismic strain accumulation and the earthquake potential on the southern San Andreas fault system. *Nature*: 441: 968-971, 2006

[12] Yuri Fialko: http://scrippsnews.ucsd.edu, 21.06.06

[13] Volcanoes can also form and erupt when two tectonic plates collide, or at locations that are far away from a fault line altogether

[14] See http://www.pbs.org/wgbh/nova/vesuvius/predict.html

[15] Jonathan M Castro and Donald B Dingwell: Rapid ascent of rhyolitic magma at Chaitén volcano, Chile. *Nature* 461: 780-783, 2009

[16] A cocktail of drugs that anaesthetise the victim, then cause muscle paralysis and heart failure

[17] Gerd Gigerenzer: *Reckoning with Risk. Learning to live with uncertainty* (Allen Lane: The Penguin Press, London, 2002), p 142 et seq

[18] *ABC of Child Protection* 4th edn. R Meadow et al. (Blackwell 2007)

[19] According to a detailed study of deaths of babies in five regions of England between 1993 and 1996

[20] Stephen J Watkins: *British Medical Journal* 320: 2-3, 2000

[21] September 2002 issue of *Plus*, published by the Univerity of Cambridge Press; see also http://plus.maths.org/issue21/features/clark/index.html

[22] *Daily Telegraph*, Sept 6, 2007

[23] Gerd Gigerenzer, p 6. See Note 17

[24] John Adams: *Risk* (UCL Press, London, 1995) p 120

[25] The cottage hospital in Clinton to which she was taken did not recognise this. The nurse thought her moaning and vomiting typical of a neurotic Englishwoman. She would have died that night from peritonitis. Fortunately I was able to move her to the hospital of Kansas University Medical School (where I had given a talk earlier in the day). It was not only the chief of surgery, who found the tear in her intestine, sewed it up and pumped her full of antibiotics, who saved her life. It was also his number two. A few days after the operation my wife developed an embolism. Her condition began to deteriorate badly (I remember her talking about a lovely velvet corridor along which she was slipping, which others in near-death situations have described in similar terms). She had to re-swallow the stomach tube without gagging and felt too tired to do so. 'Swallow, or you will die. Remember this is not Paris, New York or Monte Carlo: do you want you children to have to say their mother snuffed it in Kansas City, Kansas'? She swallowed. If you read this, thank you Dr Mahoney

[26] John Adams, p 152. See Note 24

[27] See www.safespeed.com and *Sunday Telegraph* October 21, 2007

[28] Figures from Francis Wheen: *How Mumbo-Jumbo Conquered the World. A Short History of Modern Delusions* (Fourth Estate, London, 2004), p 128

[29] Paul S Mead *et al*: Food-Related Illness and Death in the United States; see http://www.cdc.gov/ncidod/eid/vol5no5/mead.htm

[30] As of 5 April 2010; those dying of other forms of CJD greatly outnumber the vCJD victims: see http://www.cjd.ed.ac.uk/figures.htm

[31] *The Guardian*, January 10, 2007

[32]   Christopher Booker and Richard North: *Scared to Death. From BSE to Global Warming – How Scares Are Costing Us the Earth* (Continuum, London, 2007) p 126

[33]   Which is why sheep from the latter countries are used for 'biopharming': genetically engineering sheep to produce human medicinal proteins in large quantity in their milk

[34]   A Bulgarian defector killed at a bus stop in London in 1978 through the injection of a tiny amount of ricin (a protein isolated from castor beans) through the tip of an umbrella

[35]   One bite contains enough venom to kill more than 20 men

[36]   **proteinaceous infectious particle**, the **–on** being added by analogy with 'virion', a virus particle

[37]   See *Les Prix Nobel 1997* (Nobel Foundation, Stockholm, 1998) pp 262-323

[38]   Quoted by Gerd Gigerenzer, pp 5&6. See Note 17

[39]   Junjie Qin *et al*: A human gut microbial gene catalogue established by metagenomic sequencing. *Nature* 464: 59-XX, 2010

[40]   Some two billion people are in this category

[41]   In the case of malaria, permethrin-impregnated bed nets, costing around $2 each, could avoid most of the deaths caused by malaria-infested *Anopheles* insects

[42]   Mainly *Plasmodium falciparum* and *P vivax*

[43]   And are therefore at risk of succumbing to heart attack, stroke and type 2 diabetes, the form that is less insulin-dependent than type 1

[44]   See, for example, Paul Trayhurn: *Obesity: Genes, Appetite and Lifestyle*, in *Access Not Excess. The search for better nutrition* (ed Charles Pasternak, Smith-Gordon, St Ives, Cambs, 2011)

[45] Or if you subscribe to pre-natal diagnosis, to prevent an offspring carrying that mutation from being born at all

[46] Heterozygotes, who carry only one copy of the rogue gene, as opposed to homozygotes, who carry two copies of the gene, one from each parent

[47] Hamid Bolouri: *Personal Genomics and Personalized Medicine* (Imperial College Press, London, 2010) and Francis S Collins: *The Language of Life: DNA and the Revolution in Personalized Medicine* (Harper/Profile, 2010). See also Francis Collins: Has the revolution arrived? *Nature* 464: 674-675 (2010), J Craig Venter: Multiple personal genomes await, *Nature* 464: 676-677 (2010), Eric S Lander: Initial impact of the sequencing of the human genome, *Nature* 470: 187-197 (2011) and Eric D Green and Mark S Guyer: Charting a course for genomic medicine from base pairs to bedside, *Nature* 470: 204-213 (2011)

[48] Christopher Booker and Richard North, p 163. See Note 32

[49] I collected the titbits in this section from a variety of sources, the accuracy of which I am unable to confirm

[50] Quoted by Richard Cohen: *Chasing the Sun. The Epic Story of the Star That Gives Us Life* (Simon and Schuster, London, 2010), p 75

[51] Christopher Hitchens: *God is not Great. How Religion Poisons Everything* (Twelve. Hachette Book Group, New York, London, 2007), p 74

[52] Due to gravitational pulls of sun and moon

[53] Georges Charpak and Henri Broch: *Debunked! ESP, Telekinesis, and Other Pseudoscience* (trans from the original French by Bart K Holland. Johns Hopkins U Press, Baltimore, MD, 2004), p 8

[54] See www.universalacidblog

[55] See Robert Matthews in *The Washington Times* of August 18, 2003 at www.washingtontimes.com

[56] Francis Wheen, p 125. See Note 28

[57]   Gabriele Doblhammer: *The Late Life Legacy of Very Early Life* (Springer-Verlag, Berlin, 2004)

[58]   Bayes *et al*: Timing of birth and risk of multiple sclerosis in the Scottish population. *Eur Neurol* 63: 36-40, 2010

[59]   Each card displayed one of five different images, and there were five cards of each image in a pack

[60]   Georges Charpak and Henri Broch, pp 51-52. See Note 53

[61]   For an article on sleight of hand – including spoon-bending – and its relation to cognition, see Susana Martinez-Conde and Stephen L Macknik: Magic and the Brain. *Scientific American* 299: Dec 2008, pp 44-51

[62]   Georges Charpak and Henri Broch, pp 20 et seq. See Note 53

[63]   Greek for 'similar' and 'disease'

[64]   Simon Singh & Edzard Ernst: *Trick or Treatment? Alternative medicine on trial* (Bantam Press, London, 2008), p 93

[65]   In 2007, Peter Hain, the secretary of state for Northern Ireland, included homeopathy among the measures to be made available to the National Health Service in Londonderry and Belfast; see Damian Thompson: *Counterknowledge. How we surrendered to conspiracy theories, quack medicine, bogus science and fake history* (Atlantic Books, London, 2008), p 83

[66]   By Bishop William Croswell Doane, the Episcopalian bishop of Albany in the USA; taken from Damian Thompson, p 81

[67]   Institut National de la Santé et de la Recherche Médicale

[68]   'Human basophil degranulation triggered by very dilute antiserum against IgE'

[69]   See John Maddox: Maddox on the 'Benveniste affair'. *Science* 241: 585-6 (1988)

[70]   Georges Charpak and Henri Broch, p xi. See Bibliography. See Note 53

CHAPTER 3

Media hype and its consequences

The need for scientific awareness: scientists, the media, and government
A high level of awareness of science is essential in today's society. This can be acquired only through education. Otherwise, perils from scientific misinterpretations, coupled with unintended harm from a free press, risk that a political leader follows a policy that is flawed and perilous.

The HIV epidemic arrives
During the early 1980s a disease, not seen before, appeared in America and elsewhere. Many of those affected had visited Africa. Many were part of a male gay community. Many were drug addicts who satisfied their craving through injection. The last two groups overlapped in places like San Francisco. By the way that the disease spread, it appeared to be an infection of one sort or another. The symptoms were varied and not easily explained: secondary infections of almost any part of the body – skin and internal organs such as lungs and stomach – and the emergence of malignant tumours. The disease was not immediately fatal, but caused a gradual decline in the health of victims. Most were dead within ten years. Taking all these factors into account, the affliction was termed acquired immune deficiency syndrome (AIDS). Because AIDS was affecting a significant proportion of Americans, particularly gays and drug addicts, funding for research into its cause was soon in place. By 1983, a likely infectious agent was identified. It turned out to be a virus and was termed human immunodeficiency virus (HIV). Viruses come in two sorts: DNA viruses and RNA viruses. The former resemble animals, plants and bacteria in that their hereditary material is DNA. The latter are an exception to the rule that genes are made of DNA: in this case RNA replaces DNA. Such viruses are quite common. Influenza, measles, mumps and the common cold are well-known examples that affect humans; foot and mouth disease virus is an RNA virus that infects cattle and sheep. HIV proved to be an RNA virus. It works differently from the ones just mentioned, in that its RNA genome is first copied into a piece of DNA, which is then transcribed back into RNA. Such viruses are known as retroviruses. A few years on, the entire genome [1] of HIV was sequenced: the position of every unit (A: adenine, G: guanine, U: uracil and C: cytosine) within its RNA strand was established; the function of every protein produced by the virus [2] was elucidated. A scientific tour de force?

Analysis proved easier than synthesis. A quarter of a century after the isolation and characterisation of HIV, we still do not have an effective vaccine against it. This illustrates the unpredictability of producing vaccines against infectious microbes. A vaccine against smallpox virus (it happens to be a DNA one) was produced without knowing any of the details of its component DNA or proteins. By 1976 smallpox was virtually eradicated throughout the world. Today 40 million people are infected with HIV, the majority in sub-Saharan Africa. Most will eventually die of the disease.

What, you may wonder, is the reason for the susceptibility of male homosexuals and intravenous drug users to infection with HIV? If it is a sexually transmitted pathogen like gonorrhoea or syphilis, why does it affect drug users, and if it is a pathogen like tetanus that is introduced into the blood stream through an inadvertent prick of the skin, why does it affect male homosexuals? The answer is that HIV does indeed infect the host through the blood stream like tetanus, but that unlike tetanus, HIV comes not from the environment but from an infected person. In the case of drug users, someone becomes infected because the needle he or she is using has previously been employed by a person who is HIV-positive. In the case of male homosexuals, someone becomes infected because his partner, who is having anal sex with him, is HIV-positive: during anal sex, the lining of the rectum is easily ruptured and the virus enters the circulation Some years ago, a good scientific friend of mine died of AIDS. But Dimitri Papahadjopoulos was neither a homosexual nor a drug addict. Dimitri suffered from haemophilia, a disease in which one of the proteins in the sequence of reactions that leads to the clotting of blood is missing. The protein is called factor VIII, and is routinely isolated from the blood of healthy individuals. Preparations of factor VIII are injected into sufferers of haemophilia when they require it, just as insulin is injected into type 1 diabetics. Dimitri had the misfortune to have been injected with a preparation of factor VIII that had been contaminated with HIV [3]. The case of haemophiliacs shows that AIDS is a blood-borne disease.

So much for HIV infection in gays and drug addicts. What about the 25 million sub-Saharan Africans suffering from AIDS? They cannot all be male homosexuals or intravenous users. Quite so, and as a matter of fact 60% of them are women. I put this question to Luc Montagnier, a charming Frenchman who was one of the discoverers of HIV. Montagnier and I were participants at a conference in Hyderabad in 1987 to mark the opening of the new Centre for Cellular and Molecular Biology (CCMB), that has become one of the most prestigious research centres in India [4]. Montagnier's answer was evasive: 'We don't really know. I suspect it is because many AIDS victims are prostitutes, who have minor skin lesions, and who in any case are suffering from other infectious diseases that somehow interact with HIV infection. After all, we know that a failing immune system underlies AIDS'. Twenty years on, and we are still not sure of the exact aetiology of AIDS in Africa and in under-developed countries elsewhere. But Montagnier's guess that a cross-infection may be involved has been borne out. Between a quarter and a half of AIDS patients in Africa also have tuberculosis.

Montagnier's isolation and characterization of the HIV virus was recognised by the award of a Nobel Prize in 2008. But there was another player, who also correctly identified HIV as the cause of AIDS. Robert Gallo, a distinguished American scientist competed with Montagnier throughout the 1980s and 1990s. The two men fought like tigers, each claiming priority for their discovery. Everyone expected the eventual Nobel to be shared by the two contenders. It was not to be. Montagnier's award was shared with his research assistant, Françoise Barré-Sinoussi, and with a German scientist working on a totally different topic. This was Harald zu Hausen, who showed that certain papilloma viruses, that are DNA viruses, are the main cause of cervical cancer. The award of Nobel prizes can be as unpredictable as the science behind them [5].

Peter Duesberg is a brilliant scientist. At 33, working in a laboratory at the University of California at Berkeley, he was one of the first to isolate an oncogene [6] from a virus. The implications of his work, which proved to be wide-reaching, were recognised by his peers and he was duly elected to the prestigious National Academy of Sciences [7]. Duesberg studied Rous sarcoma virus, which is a retrovirus like HIV. In this case, the DNA copy of its RNA gene becomes integrated into the genetic material of its host. The expression of such a piece of DNA can result in cancer, which is why it is known as an oncogene.

In 1988 Duesberg began to publish articles suggesting that everyone had got the cause of AIDS wrong [8]. Infection with HIV is not the cause. In America, where the predominant victims are male homosexuals and drug addicts, it is their use of recreational drugs, such as alkyl nitrates that leads to AIDS. Moreover zidovudine or AZT, a medicament introduced to *combat* AIDS, is actually a cause of the disease. Since AZT proved to be of little value, it was difficult to separate the two purported actions of the drug. In Africa, where the predominant victims are neither male homosexuals nor drug addicts, failure of the immune system (which Duesberg agrees is the underlying cause of AIDS) is brought about by malnutrition and infections, some of which are the result of drinking contaminated water. Much of this, of course, is true. Whether the immune system breaks down because of 'overload' by infections, or whether a failing immune system allows infectious microbes to evade destruction, is a chicken-and-egg argument that is difficult to resolve. Duesberg's point that American AIDS and

African AIDS are different diseases has an element of truth behind it in so far as the strains of HIV that predominate in America are different to those that prevail in Africa. But that every patient with AIDS – whether in America or Africa – tests positively for HIV is irrefutable, and provides convincing evidence against Duesberg's hypothesis.

Thabo Mbeki is a Xhosa. He grew up in the Transkei (now the Eastern Cape province) of South Africa. His father, a cultured man with two university degrees, was an ardent member of the African National Congress (ANC) and the son would follow in the father's footsteps. At 14 Thabo joined the party. Three years later he was expelled from high school on account of his involvement in a student strike. He continued his studies at home, then moved to Johannesburg to work with the ANC activist Walter Sisulu. When Sisulu, Nelson Mandela and Mbeki's father were arrested and imprisoned, Thabo was ordered by the ANC to leave South Africa in order to avoid imprisonment himself. He would spend the next 28 years in exile, moving from one country to another, writing articles and broadcasting on behalf of the anti-apartheid cause, rather like the Russian revolutionaries of an earlier century. He did not need encouragement to emigrate: his father was in prison, his cousin had disappeared without trace, his brother was murdered, and his son Kwanda was killed while trying to join him abroad. First Thabo moved to England, where he studied for a master's degree in economics at Sussex University. His ANC masters were oblivious to the cold war, then at its height, between the Soviet Union and the USA. He was sent to the Soviet Union to receive military training, and to the USA to raise money for the ANC. Eventually he settled in Zambia's capital, Lusaka, which housed the headquarters of the banned ANC.

During the 1990s Mbeki returned to South Africa, where he became deputy president to Nelson Mandela. In 1997 he succeeded Mandela as president of the ANC, and two years later as President of the Republic of South Africa. Mandela was a hard act to follow, especially as Mbeki lacked the charisma and spontaneity of his predecessor. Instead he is a quiet, thoughtful, politician. Coping with South Africa's falling economy did not prove easy. From the start Mbeki decided that the country needed to adopt a Western-style market economy. Only when South Africa was able to afford it, could the redistribution of wealth begin. This was not what his superiors of the ANC, now his subjects, wished to hear. Nevertheless Mbeki stuck to his guns, and pointed to the economic chaos that his neighbour Robert Mugabe was causing in Zimbabwe, as a result of so-called wealth redistribution through the seizure of white farm-lands. Mugabe's policies were turning the fertile breadbasket of southern Africa into an unproductive desert: instead of wealth, he was delivering starvation. Mbeki would have none of this.

Wisely he continued the economic policies he had initiated. Criticism of his performance as president came mainly from outside the country: why was he supporting Mugabe against the majority view of the British Commonwealth, and not condemning him more vociferously? Again Mbeki refused to budge and his stance earned him re-election as President in 2004. On 27 June 2008 Robert Mugabe 'won' an obviously rigged presidential election in Zimbabwe. By this time agricultural production in Zimbabwe had fallen by 80%, unemployment had risen to 85%, inflation was running at more than 100 million percent per year, thousands of native Zimbabweans (as well as some Europeans) had been killed by Mugabe's 'war veterans', and three million citizens had fled the country [9]. The upstanding President of South Africa still refused to condemn his neighbour outright [10].

The media, particularly the London *Sunday Times* [10a], thought Duesberg's assertion news-worthy. One cannot disagree with that. What they failed to do, was to point out to their readers just what a maverick Duesberg had become: that his claims were scientifically flawed. The majority view, that infection with HIV is the cause of AIDS, whether in America or Africa, received scant coverage. We cannot be sure that Thabo Mbeki first became aware of Duesberg's views through reading the *Sunday Times*, but press coverage certainly helped to bring Duesberg's proposition to a wide audience. Mbeki became convinced that Duesberg was right. It was a pragmatic decision on two counts. Politically it meant that South Africans were not homosexuals, drug users, or clients of prostitutes. They were unfortunate victims of decades of oppression under the apartheid regime, that had denied them proper medical treatment, and left them malnourished and forced to drink contaminated water. Economically it meant that there was no need to invest in expensive anti-HIV drugs, or to engage in a costly campaign urging the use of condoms (that prevent transmission of HIV), which was an affront to the dignity of decent and chaste citizens. Two million men, unaware that they were HIV positive until tested in a survey, went happily about their business, engaging in sexual encounters without realising that they were passing on the disease [11]. Mind you, Mbeki had some senior clerics on his side. Cardinal Emmanuel Wamala of Uganda, and the archbishop of Nairobi, both informed their congregations that condoms actually transmit AIDS [12]. And, to inject some laughter into this depressing tale, ' ... the auxiliary bishop of Rio de Janeiro, Rafael Llano Cifuentes, told his congregation in a sermon that "the church is against condom use. Sexual relations between a man and a woman have to be natural. I have never seen a little dog using a condom during sexual intercourse with another dog"' [13].

I referred to the inefficacy of AZT as an anti-AIDS drug. Actually it was subsequently shown to be effective in one respect. When administered to a pregnant mother who is HIV positive, it prevents transmission of the virus to her soon-to-be-born offspring. And the predominant cause of AIDS in children under fifteen is precisely through this route. But when Merck, the manufacturers of AZT [14], offered the drug *free* to pregnant women in South Africa who were HIV-positive, Mbeki refused the offer. The cost of distribution and treatment he considered to be uneconomical. In any case, the treatment was worthless, as AIDS has nothing to do with HIV. So, Mbeki invited Duesberg onto a Presidential Advisory Panel on HIV and AIDS in 2000. It is difficult to work out an estimate of the number of people dying from AIDS, who *might* have been saved by AZT and condom use. Between 1997 and 2004 the annual death rate, from all natural causes, increased by nearly 80% (from 316,505 to 567,000). A large proportion of these deaths are surely attributable to AIDS. Taking a conservative estimate of 50% as being AIDS-related, this means that more than 3 million died from this cause during those seven years. If one looks at the most sexually active groups, namely women between 25 and 34 years of age and men between 30 and 44 years of age, the increased death rate in the former is *five-fold*, and in the latter almost *two-fold*. So the figure of 3 million dying from AIDS is probably an under-estimate. The number of children under 15 who are HIV positive was 240,000 in 2005 [15]. Could most of these lives have been spared, had AZT been given to their mothers? At the beginning of this chapter I said that scientific misinterpretations, together with an exuberant press, can lead to policies that are flawed and perilous. It is a lesson we would do well to take on board.

Vaccines
The Daily Mail, which enjoys one of the largest circulations in the UK [16], is extensively read by 'middle England' for its exposees of what it considers to be medical scandals. In 1998, in company with other papers, it started to warn its readers that the triple MMR vaccine, that protects against measles, mumps and rubella (German measles), is unsafe because it leads to autism. It ran this as a lead story because an article by Dr Andrew Wakefield and colleagues had appeared in the medical journal *Lancet*, pointing out that the MMR vaccine could indeed give rise to autism, as well as to a syndrome called inflammatory bowel disease (IBD). Several reasons for this outcome were suggested at the time. Three different antigens (the parts of the measles, mumps and rubella viruses that are injected) at any one time might overwhelm the body's defence mechanism. Three doses of thimerosal, a mercury-containing preservative in which vaccine is dissolved, instead of one, might be toxic. So far as the first reason is concerned, children are constantly exposed to many microbes that live in their nasal passage: a single bacterial throat infection can introduce up to 50 different antigens without any

dire consequences. As regards the second reason, the mercury in thimerosal is rapidly eliminated from the body (unlike other mercury-containing compounds) and therefore does not accumulate in the brain, as claimed. In any case, thimerosal was phased out in 1999. The incidence of autism in children born since then has remained exactly the same. In the mind of a blinkered public, though, fortified by the media, vaccines just aren't safe.

Many studies were set up after 1998 in order to examine the alleged links between MMR vaccine and autism or IBD. In 2004, for example, a survey compared 1,300 children diagnosed with autism against 4,500 controls. Whether or not the children had received the MMR vaccine made no difference to either group [17]. In 2006 a Canadian survey of 28,000 children found no effect of MMR vaccine on the incidence of bowel disease. In 2008 a study negated Dr Wakefield's suggestion that measles-specific antibodies (immune molecules) might linger in triple vaccine-injected children and subsequently trigger autism. 98 children with autism, 52 children with special educational needs, and 90 normally-developing children were tested for measles antibodies. There was no difference between any of the groups, irrespective of whether they had received the triple MMR vaccine or vaccines against measles, mumps and rubella given in single doses. Note that in his original article, Dr Wakefield had actually conceded that 'We did not prove an association between MMR vaccine and the syndrome described'. So much of the hype was generated by the media.

Even if Dr Wakefield was wrong (in May of 2010 he was struck off the medical register by the General Medical Council for serious professional misconduct), surely *The Daily Mail* and other newspapers were right in warning the public of a potential danger? Several adverse side-effects of vaccines have been described now and again so that it must be right to warn the public. Possibly, but not if the media fail to point out that your chances of falling ill after a vaccination are thousands of times less than the risk of falling very seriously ill if you are not vaccinated. Since the (single) measles vaccine was introduced in England and Wales in 1968, the incidence of measles has fallen from between 150,000 and 600,000 cases a year, with around 1,000 deaths, to just 50 cases a year, with no deaths attributable to measles at all in 1995 (in 1988 the MMR vaccine had replaced single vaccine against measles). By this time, 92% of all children had been vaccinated. But over the last decade, the percentage of children vaccinated against measles by the triple vaccine (single vaccines are not available on the National Health Service) has fallen steadily, at the same time as the incidence of measles has increased (from 56 cases in 1998 to around 1,000 in 2007, with the first death for fourteen years in 2006). The percentage of children being vaccinated is slowly coming back up, but it is still below 95%, which is the limit necessary to achieve 'herd immunity'. It takes only a few unvaccinated individuals to put the whole population at risk. In the United States, for example, someone dies unnecessarily every other day as a result of not having been vaccinated [18].

A striking example of such a situation is provided by the cessation of polio vaccination in Nigeria. For just one year, between 2003 and 2004, vaccination against polio ceased: the media had suggested that the procedure was a deliberate attempt to harm Muslims [19]. Polio is highly infectious and easily transmitted across borders by travellers. In 2005 the global incidence of polio jumped by 50%, having spread to previously polio-free countries as distant from Nigeria as Somalia, Yemen and Indonesia. 94% of the new cases were traced back to Nigeria.

The anti-MMR campaign has resulted in a general fear of vaccination, that is coupled to public ignorance on this topic. A survey carried out in the UK in 2007 [20] found that

- One in five people believe that polio has been eradicated from the world (it hasn't)

- Two thirds of people don't know whether smallpox has been eradicated from the world (it has)

- Two out of five believe that malaria is a vaccine-preventable disease (it isn't: we're still waiting)

- Almost two thirds don't know that typhoid is a vaccine-preventable disease (it is)

- One in ten believe that HIV/AIDS is a vaccine-preventable disease (it isn't: we're still waiting)

The fourth of these findings is particularly worrying, at a time when more and more tourists visit areas where infectious diseases are endemic, thus bringing pathogenic microbes back to their home country. In the UK, cases of typhoid due to this cause have increased by almost 70% in just five years. Travellers should learn from the example of Lady Mary Wortley Montague, the high-spirited wife of the British Minister in Constantinople in the mid-eighteenth century. She used the opportunity of life in the frontier city between Europe and Asia to discover how the Circassian maidens in the sultan's seraglio protected their fair skin against the disfiguring scars of smallpox (her brother had died of the disease). The technique was to scoop up the pus from a victim of the disease, and then to sniff it up one's nose. Like so many other novel ideas, variolation, as the practice was called, is said to have been discovered by the Chinese many centuries earlier, and brought back along the silk road (together with porcelain and plague). Boldly Lady Mary instructed her young son to ape the concubines. He never developed smallpox, but of course might not have done so anyway. Lady Mary was indeed a lady before her time. She advocated a seven-year 'break clause' in any marriage (her husband was a rather dull old buffer) and it was said of her that 'the whiff of scandal clung to her like an expensive eau de cologne'.

If you still harbour doubts about vaccination, just have a look at Table 3.1 overleaf. Convinced? Good. I'll have earned my staff of Aesculapius if I can cure the syndrome of ignorance and confusion about vaccines in just a couple of paragraphs.

GM crops

Andhra Pradesh in southern India is known as the 'rice bowl of India'. There is only one problem. The increasing scarcity of freshwater for irrigating the paddy fields [21] means that farmers are unable to plant this water-demanding crop year on year. Instead they are now planting rice one year, and corn (maize), which requires less water, the next. But the yields from corn are low because of infestation with weeds. Ploughing the land before planting helps, but it is costly. A recent innovation has been to use herbicide-resistant corn seed. This means that non-specific weed-killers can be used, and there is no need for tillage between crops [22]. As a result, farmers have been able to increase their income: corn yields a profit of $242 per acre, compared with $152 per acre for rice (2005 prices). The environment benefits because the amount of freshwater used for irrigation is reduced. What I have just described – 'Zero tillage corn in coastal Andhra Pradesh helps farmers overcome water shortages' – is an example of the kind of project that Monsanto subsidizes [23]. Of course it benefits the company because the herbicide-resistant corn [24] (and the herbicide) are produced by them. So what? The farmers are economically better off and the environment improves. Genetically-modified (GM) crops benefit everyone.

The media [25] and various pressure groups take a diferent view. GM products are 'Frankenstein foods' that are a serious liabilty to our health. As I have pointed out elsewhere [26], this is nonsense. The difference between a GM product such as corn and its unmodified counterpart is that the GM variety contains an extra bit of DNA (a gene), and some extra proteins made in response to that gene. When we eat any food, whether corn on the cob, a potato, an apple, an egg, a piece

Table 3.1: Reduction of disease incidence in the UK following the introduction of vaccination. Reproduced from uvig (UK Vaccine Industry Group): *Valuing Vaccines: and investment for our future. Part I. Vaccines: myths and reality* (2007), Table 1

Disease	Last year before vaccination			After vaccination		
	Year	Deaths (all ages)	Cases (all ages)	Year	Deaths (all ages)	Cases (all ages)
Diphtheria	1939	2,133	47,061	2003	0	4
Tuberculosis	1952	10,590	48,093	2005	334	8,113†
Polio	1955	241	6,000	2003	0	0
Whooping cough	1956	92	92,410	2003	2	227‡
Tetanus	1960	32	§	2003	1	10
Measles*	1967	99	460,407	2004	0	191 ||
Mumps*	1989	0	20,713	2004	0	8,130 ||
Rubella*	1989	0	14,570	2004	0	17 ||
Hib meningitis	1991	24	840	2003	14¶	280
Meningitis C	1998	101	854	2003	19	100

Table adapted from figures provided by Dr. David Elliman, St Georges Health Authority and Helen Bedford, Institute of Child Health

*MMR vaccine since 1988; † 2005 data [21]; ‡ Data from Health Protection Agency website (www.hpa.org.uk)[22]; Laboratory confirmed cases of pertussis infection in England and Wales by quarter 2003; § Data not available; || Data from Health Protection Agency [23]; ¶ This was before the Hib catch-up campaign and the highest ever level since introduction of the vaccine in 1992

of cod or a slice of ham, the DNA and protein inside the food are broken down in the digestive tract. The end products are the four building blocks (A, C, G and T) of DNA and the twenty building blocks or amino acids (alanine, arginine, asparagine, and so on) of proteins. These building blocks are the same in all plants and animals. Whether you eat a carrot or a crayfish, a chick-pea or a chicken, a GM tomato or a regular tomato, the same four bases (A, C, G and T) and the same twenty amino acids (alanine, arginine, asparagine, and so on) will be absorbed into the blood stream. The origin of the DNA and proteins is completely irrelevant. So any particular GM food is as nutritive, or as unpalatable, as its non-GM version.

On the other hand, some proteins are able to elicit an immune response before they are degraded in the gut. This is how the oral polio vaccine works. Moreover some people develop an allergic response when eating food like peanuts, chocolate or products made from wheat. So in principle an aberrant protein in a GM crop could initiate such a reaction. Yet of the millions of people who have been consuming GM products on a daily basis throughout the USA, Argentina, Canada and China for more than a decade (often without realising it), not a single one has suffered an allergic reaction of the type I have described. In the USA, for example, more than 70% of all processed foods consumed on a daily basis are genetically modified. Some 90% of soybean oil is altered in this way. You can be sure that in the most litigious country in the world, had anyone consistently fallen ill from eating any of these products, they would have hired a lawyer and we would know about it. Of course thousands of people a day fall ill as a result of eating different foods, GM or not. The Centers for Disease Control and Prevention in the USA estimate that 325,000 people a year are hospitalised, and 5,000 die, from food-related illnesses. Generally this is due to some microbial contamination [27]. No scientifically valid publication that I am aware of has documented an allergic or other response caused specifically by eating a GM variety of food.

Where debate is justified, is in the environmental consequences of sowing GM crops [28]. In the USA, 57.7 million hectares (143 million acres) were devoted to growing GM crops (soybeans, maize, cotton, squash, papaya, alfalfa, potato, canola) in 2007. A similar area was under cultivation that year in the rest of the world: Argentina, Brazil, Canada, India, China, Paraguay. South Africa, Uruguay, Philippines, Australia, Spain and Mexico (in decreasing order) [29]. Apart from Spain, Europe isn't even on the radar. On the one hand, destroying the weeds that accompany crops, makes the environment less desirable for birds and insects (that eat broad-leaved weeds and their seeds). On the other hand the Food and Agriculture Organization (FAO) of the UN came to the conclusion in 2004 that 'Thus far, in those countries where transgenic crops have been grown, there have been no verifiable reports of them causing any *significant* health or environmental harm ... On the contrary, some important environmental and social benefits are emerging. Farmers are using less pesticide and replacing toxic chemicals with less harmful ones. As a result farm workers and water supplies are protected from poisons, and beneficial insects and birds are returning to farmers' fields' [30]. The following year it was shown that herbicide-resistant GM sugar beet is beneficial, because it helps birds to survive the winter better [31]. Then there is the chance of GM seeds being blown into a neighbouring field. If you appreciate the benefits of weed-resistant, pest-resistant, drought-resistant, or otherwise improved crops, you will be delighted. If you are a 'Greenpeace' protestor, used to destroying swathes of GM crops for no good reason, you will not. But do not think that organic farming – often promoted as an alternative to GM crops, even though it requires twice the amount of land – is going to help the Third World: as an eminent plant scientist, Dr Channapatna Prakash (Professor of Plant Molecular Genetics at Tuskegee University, Alabama, USA) has said: 'The only thing sustainable about organic farming in the developing world is that it sustains poverty and malnutrition'.

I was recently asked in the *Today* programme [32] what good GM foods do in Britain. 'Little', I responded. 'In well-off countries like the UK or the USA' – it was just before the sub-prime mortgage crisis and its financial fall-out hit us – 'we can choose what we grow: regular food, organic food, GM food. Nutritionally they're pretty much equal. But we should set an example. Britain is responsible for just 2% of global carbon dioxide emissions, and whether we plant wind machines or water melons in our garden isn't going to make much difference to global warming. But we're being asked to watch our carbon foot prints (see chapter 4) as carefully as our cholesterol levels. We must lead by example. The same is true of GM foods. We must engage in research on GM technology and encourage African nations to adopt it' [33]. The interviewer was not convinced. He seemed unaware that the yields of staple foods like maize and sweet potato in Africa are less than half the world average, that this is largely due to infestations by weeds, pests, drought and spoilage on the way to market, and that GM seeds resistant to weeds, pests, drought and spoilage are now in development. No one has died as a result of media hype over GM, but the paucity of its application in Africa continues to maintain malnutrition across that unfortunate continent [34].

The GM controversy erupted again in England in May of 2012, when a group of protesters calling themselves Take the Flour Back threatened to trash an experimental crop of wheat grown by Rothamsted Research in Harpenden, Hertfordshire. The institute also suffered a cyber attack on its website. What caused the protesters' rage was the introduction into the wheat of a compound that repels aphids (greenfly and blackfly) in order to avoid having to spray crops with pesticide. The compound – an alarm pheromone – occurs naturally in wild potato and is entirely without effect on humans.

The possibility of the experimental crop infecting adjoining pasture was minimal. As the scientists pointed out, 'Our new wheat plants contain genes copied from nature and are planted in a highly controlled field trial that has been thoroughly evaluated, inspected and risk-assessed by independent scientists and government. The risk of cross-pollination was judged negligible. All experts agree wheat is self-pollinated not wind or insect pollinated. Wheat flowers fertilise themselves before they open. The pollen, which is heavy, only lives for a few hours and falls to the ground around the plant. Furthermore, this is a very small scale trial eight 6m x 6m plots. The smell the new plants make already occurs naturally in the aroma of more than 400 plant species including apples, hops and mint' [34a].

A heavy police presence on the day of the protest prevented the activists from tearing up the experimental crop, but their objections to GM technology continue. It's impossible to convince a group of determined agitators to remove their blinkers. The approach must be to instil a sense of the science behind GM technology into the minds of the public at large. Only then will the *agent provocateurs* behind the Green movement be rewarded with the kind of recognition extended to members of the International Flat Earth Society.

Health foods
Advertisements sustain newspapers, television networks and internet search engines such as Google and MSN. The health food business, worth billions, advertises freely. Herbal products alone are worth £200 million per year. The media are therefore complicit partners in spreading hype about the benefits of health foods. St John's wort and lemon balm for depression, sage and Chinese angelica for the menopause, white willow and tumeric for arthritis, meadowsweet and marshmallow for stomach upsets, red clover and nettle leaf for eczema, ginseng for infections and stress, ginko to improve short-term memory, green tea to burn fat, glucosamine for aching joints. If you wish to accompany your consumption of these plants with visual images of their flowers and seeds, leaves and stems, there is a superbly illustrated book [35] for you to enjoy. Don't rely on it for information, though. Despite its sub-title of *The science behind herbal remedies and nutrition*, it fails to mention cinchona (source of quinine), foxglove (source of digoxin) or limes (source of vitamin C), that have been used – to much greater effect than those listed – against malaria, heart failure and scurvy respectively for over two hundred years. Then there are vitamin supplements and omega 3 fatty acids to improve your health. If you are an average person, eating

a normal diet, the chances are that health foods and extra vitamins will make no difference to your physical health at all. Of course the placebo effect may make you think that swallowing pills and pastilles, sucking lozenges and sipping concoctions made from natural sources, have done you good: that they have improved your metabolism, reversed the loss of hair, aided your memory, reversed your depression. To the extent that positive thinking is beneficial (see chapter 5), they may do. And if you are not eating a wholesome diet, the added vitamins will certainly help. Just as much as ingesting them in the form of a succulent piece of liver [36], a plate of spinach or a bowl of cereal. But don't think that they will give you extra energy when you are feeling low. Energy comes from the caloric content of what you eat – carbohydrate, fat or protein – and health foods don't contain much of these.

These are all dogmatic statements, you will rightly point out, not backed up by statistical studies. I agree, but equally there are few controlled trials showing that health foods do have the effect they claim. Only three out of 1,345 research papers on this topic proved to have have been carried out by proper randomized, 'double blind' trials [37]. As the authors of *Trick or Treatment?* point out [38], it was Hippocrates who said: 'There are, in fact, two things, science and opinion; the former begets knowledge, the latter ignorance.' So even 2,000 years ago, people were advised not to rely on someone's opinion as to whether a new treatment works, but to test it scientifically. You can forget all the 'proven to be effective ...' and 'ninety percent of people taking this product confirm that ...' on the packet: most have no proof that stands up to scientific scrutiny, and the confirmation of efficacy is anecdotal. You can say I'm biased. When I approached the manufacturer of a well-known health product for a donation to my charity, he didn't sign a cheque. Instead he presented me with five boxes of his capsules, enough for a 6-month trial as I recall, and a large umbrella displaying the name of his product. The umbrella was useful – I live in England, after all – but the capsules designed to boost my well-being had the opposite effect. A negative placebo or nocebo, if you like. I'd hardly swallowed one (I may have taken two to ensure a good result) when a distinct feeling of nausea swept over me. The screen of my lap-top began to shimmer and I stopped work. The boxes are still in my cupboard. Would you like some?

I cannot end this short discussion without referring to some very welcome statements that have begun to appear in the media in recent years. You see that I am not biased after all. The following examples are taken pretty much at random [39].

Herbal medicine 'may do more harm than good'. A review carried out by Drs Edzard Ernst (UK's only professor of

Complementary Medicine) and Peter Canter found that many herbal products imported from China were contaminated with agricultural chemicals and other compounds [40].

Supermarkets 'mislead us over omega 3 claims'. A survey by 2,405 members of *Which?* found that 45% of their members would be more likely to buy a product if it claimed to be high in omega 3. 'Omega' compounds refer to unsaturated fatty acids, such as linolenic (omega 3), arachidonic (omega 6) and linoleic (another omega 6), that the body cannot synthesise, but that it requires in order to produce essential hormones. Natural products contain a mixture of several such fatty acids, some that the body needs, others that are without benefit. Yet half of the products claiming high levels of 'omega 3' either contained so little that they were without value, or contained the wrong sort of 'omega 3'. 'So Good Soya Essential Omega 3', for example contains less than 0.002% of the right omega 3: you'd have to drink 22 litres to derive any benefit – a quantity not advertised on the packet [41].

Vitamin pills 'can increase the risk of early death'. A review, by researchers at Copenhagen University, of 67 studies involving 230,000 healthy subjects, found 'no convincing evidence' that anti-oxidant supplements like vitamins A and E helped to prolong life expectancy. On the contrary, some had the opposite effect [42].

'The old wives' cures that could make illness worse'. A study by FSB Care, an offshoot of the Federation of Small Businesses, found that many widely held beliefs are plain wrong [43]. Vitamin C, for example, does not cure the common cold, despite having been promoted over decades by Linus Pauling to do so. Pauling was one of the few people who have won two Nobel Prizes: one for Chemistry (the nature of the covalent bond that holds the atoms of a molecule together) and one for Peace (he was an ardent opponent of nuclear weapons). He might nearly have won a third, which would have been unique. It was only an elementary mistake (of chemistry, as it happens) that prevented him from coming out with the right structure of DNA before Watson and Crick did so in 1953. Pauling was partly right about vitamin C, though. It does appear to boost your immune system, thereby improving your ability to fight off an infection, such as the common cold. But you would need to have taken the vitamin (which of course is present anyway in oranges and other citrus fruit) over a long period first. Quaffing a preparation once a cold has started is ineffective.

Misleading press reports and governmental action (or inaction) have led to loss of life in regard to HIV infectivity and the disregard of proven vaccination programmes. Failure to adopt GM crop technology may not have led to anyone's death (detractors argue the opposite), and ineffective health foods generally don't kill you either, but all four topics have one theme in common: a wilful misunderstanding of science.

Already four hundred years ago, Samuel Butler [44] encapsulated the message of this chapter: 'The most important service rendered by the press and the magazines is that of educating people to approach printed matter with distrust.'

Notes

[1]   It proved to consist of nine genes

[2]   There are 19 different proteins

[3]   Nowadays blood is routinely screened for the presence of HIV before it is used to prepare factor VIII. Even better, the factor is produced by means of genetic engineering that does not involve human blood at all

[4]   I well remember being impressed by the remarks of Rajiv Gandhi, then prime minister, in his opening speech: 'the information technology revolution is on, and it is a war we must win'. Two decades on, this is precisely what India has achieved

[5]   See Robin A Weiss: Chronicles of a killer virus. *Nature* 482: 468 (2012), a review of Nicoli Nattrass: *The AIDS Conspiracy: Science Fights Back* (Columbia University Press, 2012), Jacques Pepin: *The Origins of AIDS* (Cambridge University Press, 2011) and Victoria Harden: *AIDS at 30: A History* (Potomac Books, 2012)

[6]   A gene that gives rise to cancer, 'onco' being Greek for a lump or tumour

[7]   Harvey Bialy: *Oncogenes, Aneuploidy and AIDS: A Scientific Life and Times of Peter Duesberg* (North Atlantic Books, Berkeley CA, 2004)

[8]   Duesberg, P. H.: HIV is not the cause of AIDS. *Science*: 241: 514-516 (1988)

[9]   Though inside the country, Robert Mugabe had built a $9 million home for himself; the roof was a donation from China. See David Smith: *The Dragon and the Elephant. China, India and the New World Order* (Profile Books, London, 2007; paperback 2008), p 127

[10]   See Joshua Hammer: *The Reign of Thuggery* in *NY Review of Books*, June 26, 2008, pp 26-29

[10a] Schmidt, W. E.: British paper and science journal clash on AIDS. *NY Times* Dec 10, 1993; taken from http://en.wikipedia.org/wiki/AIDS_denialism

[11]   From the December 2006 AIDS Epidemic Uptake, prepared by UNAIDS and WHO, and published as UNAIDS/06.29E

[12]   According to author Christopher Hitchens: *God is not Great. How Religion Poisons Everything* (Twelve. Hachette Book Group, New York, London, 2007), p 46

[13]   Ibid, p 45

[14]   The drug had been developed by Burroughs Wellcome, but when it proved inactive, the company was happy to license it to Merck

[15]   These figures are all taken from the WHO December 2006 AIDS Epidemic Uptake: http://www.who.int/hiv/mediacentre/2006_EpiUpdate_en.pdf

[16]   I ought to know: my daughter is well paid for her articles

[17]   E Fombonne *et al*: Pervasive developmental disorders in Montreal, Quebec, Canada: prevalence and links with immunizations, *Paediatrics* 118: e139-e150, 2006; quoted in uvig (UK Vaccine Industry Group): *Valuing Vaccines: and investment for our future. Part I. Vaccines: myths and reality* (2007)

[18]   http://www.jennymccarthybodycount.com/Jenny_McCarthy_Body_Count/ Preventable_Deaths.html; see also Paul A Offit: *Deadly Choices: How the Anti-Vaccine Movement Threatens Us All* (Basic Books, New York, 2011)

[19]   The country is roughly divided between Muslims in the north and non-Muslims (including Christians) in the south. Islamic leaders decided that there was an American conspiracy to sterilise Muslims, and issued a fatwa in response; see Damian Thompson: *Counterknowledge. How we surrendered to conspiracy theories, quack medicine, bogus science and fake history* (Atlantic Books, London, 2008), p 20

[20]   uvig (UK Vaccine Industry Group): *A Third of the UK doesn't understand importance of vaccination* (2007); see http://www.uvig.org/Press_Releases/articles/A_Third_of_the_UK_doesnt_understand_importance_of_vaccination.html

[21]   Quirin Schiermeier: Satellite data show Indian water stocks shrinking. *Nature* 460: 789, 2009

[22]   This also has an environmental benefit as it reduces erosion and encourages carbon sequestration (see the section on climate change in Chapter 4)

[23]   Every year Monsanto makes a number of 'Pledge Awards' to farmers and others throughout the world in recognition of their efforts. These awards are judged by an international panel with widely divergent backgrounds, none of whom has any connections with Monsanto, as I can personally confirm. In 2005, for example, each of the seven winners received a $15,000 grant, payable to a non-profit organisation of their choice. Such support enables farmers and others living in a developing country to make substantial and beneficial changes to their agricultural practice

[24]   Genetically modified in such a way that a non-specific weed-killer like glyphosate or 'round-up' can be used without harm to the crop, because a glyphosate-resistant gene has been inserted. Extensive use of glyphosate represents no threat to humans (or animals), because we lack the metabolic pathway (common to most plants) that glyphosate inhibits

[25]   See, for example, the *Daily Mail* of March 10, 2004: Frankenstein food? You'll be made to like it

[26]   Charles Pasternak: *Quest: The Essence of Humanity* (Wiley, Chichester, 2003), pp 315-318, *Sunday Times* March 14, 2004 (I am not one to let earlier bias by this newspaper in regard to HIV/AIDS stand in the way of a published article) and *Sunday Express* April 3, 2011

[27] One of the aims of GM technology is to avoid precisely this: spoilage-resistant tomatoes would be of huge benefit in hot climates, for example

[28] See, for example, Emily Waltz: Battlefield. *Nature* 461: 27-32, 2009

[29] Mark A Pollack and Gregory C Shaffer: *When Cooperation Fails. The International Law and Politics of Genetically Modified Foods* (Oxford University Press, Oxford, 2009) p 300

[30] Ibid, p 35

[31] *Daily Telegraph* of Jan 19, 2005

[32] A UK breakfast radio show that covers topical issues

[33] Instead of the reverse: see, eg, Robert Paarlberg: *Starved for Science: How Biotechnology is Being Kept Out of Africa* (Harvard U Press, 2008)

[34] N E Nyange *et al*: *Biotechnology for sustainable agriculture, food security and poverty reduction in Africa*; in *Access Not Excess. The search for better nutrition* (ed Charles Pasternak, Smith-Gordon and Company, St Ives, Cambs, 2011)

[34a] From *The Guardian* of 1 June 2012; see http://www.guardian.co.uk/environment/2012/jun/01/letter-take-flour-back-rothamsted

[35] J G Vaughan & P A Judd: *The Oxford Book of Health Foods.* (Oxford U Press, Oxford, 2003)

[36] I appreciate that many in the USA consider liver, kidney, sweetbread (pancreas) and other animal organs as offal, fit only for one's pets

[37] *Daily Telegraph* October 4, 2007

[38] Simon Singh & Edzard Ernst: *Trick or Treatment? Alternative medicine on trial* (Bantam Press, London, 2008), p 1

[39] All refer to articles from the *Daily Telegraph* (as do many throughout this book); this is merely because it is the paper to which the centre in which I

have my office subscribes. The same reports would be found in other publications like *The Times*, *The Independent* or the *Guardian*

[40]   *Daily Telegraph* October 4, 2007

[41]   *Daily Telegraph* October 25, 2007; see also *The Times* September 30, 2009 for a letter by 19 internationally renowned scientists

[42]   *Daily Telegraph* April 16, 2008

[43]   *Daily Telegraph* April 19, 2008

[44]   British poet and satirist (1612-1680)

CHAPTER 4

Unpalatable truths: scientists wear blinkers too

Climate change

The plane banked sharply as it began its descent into Cleveland Hopkins airport. At that moment the rays of the setting sun lit up the shoreline of the lake in a bright glow of orange and crimson. The next minute the colours had changed to silvery blue on the lake beside the rapidly darkening green of the flat countryside beside it. Nature always reassures me. I put out of my mind the phrase my hostess had used in her letter to me – ladies who winter in Palm Beach don't do emails – some weeks previously. 'We've decided to move your talk from the Twenty-First Century Club to a member's home: it will provide a nicer atmosphere', which I had translated to 'Only a handful have signed up for the event'. Soon I was being driven along country lanes to the Chagrin Valley Hunt Club, where I would be staying. The charming name of the stream that winds its way into Lake Eerie is probably not French, but is derived from the Indian 'Sha-ga-rin', meaning 'clear water' (which it is). The club lives up to its name. Not more than an inch separates one picture from the next along its corridors and rooms: all depict gentlemen in hunting pink, or slavering hounds, or an occasional fox looking sadly out of its frame.

The following evening we were having drinks in the library. Although it was early May, a fire of logs burned in the grate. I could have been in Leicestershire. My hostess was introducing me to the husbands of the ladies who had listened to me earlier. I had spoken in a room that gave on to a manicured garden leading down to a sizeable lake. It was large enough to accommodate a hundred folding chairs: to my surprise, every one had been occupied. My thoughts snapped back to the tall, steely-eyed man who was addressing me. 'I would like to have listened to your talk. What is your view about global warming?' My subject had actually been 'What makes us human?', and I wasn't quite prepared for this change of tack. 'Well,' I began, when he interrupted me. 'It's all nonsense. I've been going down to our place in Palm Beach and measuring the temperature' – I wasn't quite sure whether he was referring to the ocean or the air – 'and I can tell you that it hasn't budged over the past 10 years.' Several guests within earshot were nodding their heads in agreement.

The previous week, in my hotel room in downtown Los Angeles, I had switched on the television set – it was the size of a small car – and tuned in to the

National Geographic Channel. A beautiful white polar bear sits on the edge of the ice. Water laps at his feet. Is he about to plunge into the Arctic waters, to return with a fat seal that will sustain him for several months? He doesn't look happy, though. The camera has managed to catch a worried look on his furry face. Ah, notice that behind him ice is breaking off. Soon his resting place will be a mere floe. As that begins to melt, he will have nowhere to eat his meal. In fact he will have nowhere to live. He will drown. The Arctic ice sheet is slowly breaking up. If you want to make a summer expedition to the North Pole in 50 years time, it seems, you will need a boat, not skis. This applies only during the summer months, of course, when most of the Arctic ice melts. Although polar bears can live on dry land (together with their brown cousins), they cannot survive for long on the scraps of food available on land. They need to hunt seals, and to do so, they need to attack them from the edge of the ice: in the open water, seals will out-swim any polar bear.

Back in London, I am lunching with Christopher Booker, an inspiring author and incisive journalist who writes a weekly column for the *Sunday Telegraph*. 'Even the scientists admit that they have got their figures wrong. NASA had to revise their GISS [1] monthly US surface temperatures, when it was pointed out that they had neglected distortion from the "heat island effect"[2]. The hottest year of the 20th century was not 1998, as originally claimed and widely reported in the press, but 1934.' He reminds me that last winter was the coldest for several decades in the northern hemisphere: snow in Jerusalem, Damascus and Amman is not a normal accompaniment to the festive season. All four major global temperature tracking outlets (Hadley, NASA's GISS, UAH, RSS) confirm that the drop in temperature, between $0.65\,^{\circ}\mathrm{C}$ and $0.75\,^{\circ}\mathrm{C}$, was sufficient to wipe out most of the warming recorded over the past hundred years [3]. As for the melting of the Arctic ice cap and the plight of the polar bears, it seems that sea ice in January of 2008 was the same as that a year previously (around 13 million sq km); during the intervening summer, 75% of the ice had indeed melted, but all of it refroze subsequently [4]. And new evidence shows that around 90 million years ago, when dinosaurs were still around and crocodiles inhabited the Arctic regions, with ocean temperatures in excess of $35\,^{\circ}\mathrm{C}$, an Antarctic ice sheet roughly half its present size, nevertheless persisted for some 200,000 years [5].

I cannot disregard the top scientists of the world. In 2005, the presidents of the science academies of Brazil, Canada, China, France, Germany, India, Italy, Japan, UK and USA signed a joint statement [6]. The opening paragraph read 'There will always be uncertainty in understanding a system as complex as the world's climate. However there is now strong evidence that significant global warming is occurring. The evidence comes from direct measurements of rising surface air temperatures and subsurface ocean temperatures and from phenomena such as increases in average global sea levels, retreating glaciers, and changes to many physical and biological systems. It is likely that most of the warming in recent decades can be attributed to human activities. This warming has already led to changes in the Earth's climate.

'The existence of greenhouse gases in the atmosphere is vital to life on Earth – in their absence average temperatures would be about 30 $^{\circ}$C lower than they are today. But human activities are now causing atmospheric concentrations of greenhouse gases – including carbon dioxide, methane, tropospheric ozone, and nitrous oxide – to rise well above pre-industrial levels. Carbon dioxide (CO_2) levels have increased from 280 ppm in 1750 to over 375 ppm today – higher than any previous levels that can be reliably measured (ie in the last 420,000 years). Increasing greenhouse gases are causing temperatures to rise; the Earth's surface warmed by approximately 0.6 $^{\circ}$C over the twentieth century... .

'Action taken now to reduce significantly the build-up of greenhouse gases in the atmosphere will lessen the magnitude and rate of climate change ... .'

The following year Al Gore echoed this warning with a film and book [7] on the subject. 'At stake is the survival of our civilization and the habitability of the Earth. Or, as one eminent scientist put it, the pending question is whether the combination of an opposable thumb and a neocortex is a viable combination on this planet ... Spring is coming earlier; fall is arriving later. And all the while, the temperature keeps going up – more rapidly in the Arctic than anywhere else in the world ... The number of peer-reviewed articles dealing with ''climate change'' published in scientific journals during the previous 10 years: 928. The percentage of articles in doubt as to the causes of global warming: 0%. The percentage of articles in the popular press that doubt the cause of global warming: 53% (out of 636).' Clearly someone else who considers the media guilty of blinkering an unsuspecting public. A man worthy of the Nobel Peace Prize. I put out of my mind the bizarre criteria for this honour. Mahatma Ghandi's nomination for the award was turned down. Though he was 'obviously the greatest personality proposed ... an apostle of peace, he is also a nationalist' [8]. Since then, not only nationalists, but former terrorists (Menachem Begin: 1978 and Yasser Arafat: 1994) have received the prize; and Hitler was on the short list for 1938 [9]. Still, well done Al Gore.

Then a colleague draws my attention to the fact that a British court has ruled against the government, which had promoted the showing of Al Gore's film to school children. Nine inaccuracies were noted:

The film claims that melting snows on Mount Kilimanjaro are evidence of global warming. The Government's expert was forced to concede that this is not correct.

The film suggests that evidence from ice cores proves that rising CO_2 causes temperature increases over 650,000 years. The Court found that the film was misleading: over that period the rises in CO_2 lagged behind the temperature rises by 800-2000 years.

The film uses emotive images of Hurricane Katrina and suggests that it has been caused by global warming. The Government's expert had to accept that it was 'not possible' to attribute one-off events to global warming.

The film shows the drying up of Lake Chad and claims that this was caused by global warming. The Government's expert had to accept that this was not the case.

The film claims that a study showed that polar bears had drowned due to disappearing arctic ice. It turned out that Mr Gore had misread the study: in fact four polar bears drowned and this was because of a particularly violent storm.

The film threatens that global warming could stop the Gulf Stream, throwing Europe into an ice age: the Claimant's evidence was that this was a scientific impossibility.

The film blames global warming for species losses including coral reef bleaching. The Government could not find any evidence to support this claim.

The film suggests that sea levels could rise by 7 m causing the displacement of millions of people. In fact the evidence is that sea levels are expected to rise by about 40 cm over the next hundred years and that there is no such threat of massive migration.

The film claims that rising sea levels have caused the evacuation of certain Pacific islands to New Zealand. The Government are unable to substantiate this and the Court observed that this appears to be a false claim.

In the USA, Marlo Lewis, a senior fellow of the Competitive Enterprise Institute in Washington, DC points to statements in the film that are either one-sided, misleading, exaggerated, speculative or plain wrong [10]. Among the latter, the film

- claims that glaciologist Lonnie Thompson's reconstruction of climate history proves the Medieval Warm Period was 'tiny' compared to the warming observed in recent decades. It doesn't. Four of Thompson's six ice cores indicate that the Medieval Warm Period was as warm as, or warmer than, any recent decade.

- claims that the rate of global warming is accelerating, when it has been remarkably constant for the past 30 years – roughly 0.17 °C/decade.

- attributes Europe's killer heat wave of 2003 to global warming; it was actually due to an atmospheric circulation anomaly.

- claims that 2004 set an all-time record for the number of tornadoes in the United States. Tornado frequency has not increased; rather, the detection of smaller tornadoes has increased. If we consider the tornadoes that have been detectable for many decades (F-3 or greater), there is actually a downward trend since 1950.

Needless to say, some of these criticisms have themselves been criticised by others. Science is not as clear-cut a process as many believe: perfectly valid observations may be subject to quite different interpretations. We all know that to make a point, you sometimes have to exaggerate a little. The latest report of the International Panel on Climate Change (IPCC) that appeared in 2007, is more measured. The IPCC is a global consortium of more than 700 scientists, mathematicians, sociologists and others who act as lead authors, contributing authors and expert peer reviewers. None is a politician or a journalist. For the past two decades they have been drawing up models, based on measurements from weather balloons (atmospheric pressure, temperature and humidity) and ice cores (carbon dioxide levels [11]), from tree rings and corals, from temperatures at the surface of the earth and in the oceans, from sea levels across the five continents, from records of snow cover and glacier movement, in order to draw conclusions about how the climate is changing, and whether this is due to human factors. The 2007 report alone consists of over 12 chapters totalling more than ten thousand pages of carefully argued scenarios, peppered with tables and diagrams, and supported by references to peer-reviewed articles in scientific journals. The final chapter is a 'Summary for Policy Makers'. It states [12] that 'Warming of the climate system is unequivocal, as is now evident from observations of increased global average air and ocean temperatures, widespread melting of snow and ice, and rising global average sea level. ... Most of the observed increase in globally averaged temperatures since the mid twentieth century is *very likely* due to the observed increases in anthropogenic' (ie man-made) 'greenhouse gas concentrations', the chief culprit being carbon dioxide. Furthermore 'There is *high agreement* and *much evidence* that ... global greenhouse gas emissions will grow over the next few decades' and that this will 'cause further warming ... .'

Some of the very same members of the IPPC, though, have expressed their concerns about the way the 'Summary for Policy Makers' is drawn up. 'Skepticism, a hallmark of science, is frowned upon ... We are not told here that the assertion (that global warming over the past 50 years is due to humans) is based on computer model output, not direct observation. The simple fact is we don't have thermometers marked with "this much is human-caused" and "this much is natural"' [13]. Others have challenged matters of fact in the IPCC report [14], and continue to do so.

Later in 2007, the UN held a conference on climate change in Bali. *Bloomberg News* calculated that the government officials and others who flew to Bali engendered as much pollution as 20,000 cars in a year, or the equivalent of the entire annual emission from an African country like Chad. Just before the conference, more than 90 scientists, including professors of atmospheric sciences, climatology, computer modelling, economics, engineering, geochemistry, geophysics, marine geology, meteorology, oceanography, palaeoclimatology and physics wrote an open letter to the Secretary-General of the UN, Ban Ki-Moon (see http://scienceandpublicploicy.org/reprint/open_letter_to_un.html). They called it 'Don't fight, adapt'. The letter stated:

> It is not possible to stop climate change, a natural phenomenon that has affected humanity through the ages. Geological, archaeological, oral and written histories all attest to the dramatic challenges posed to past societies from unanticipated changes in temperature, precipitation, winds and other climatic variables. We therefore need to equip nations to become resilient to the full range of these natural phenomena by promoting economic growth and wealth generation.
>
> The United Nations Intergovernmental Panel on Climate Change (IPCC) has issued increasingly alarming conclusions about the climatic influences of human-produced carbon dioxide (CO_2), a non-polluting gas that is essential to plant photosynthesis. While we understand the evidence that has led them to view CO_2 emissions as harmful, the IPCC's conclusions are quite inadequate as justification for implementing policies that will markedly diminish future prosperity. In particular, it is not established that it is possible to significantly alter global climate through cuts in human greenhouse gas emissions. On

top of which, because attempts to cut emissions will slow development, the current UN approach of CO_2 reduction is likely to increase human suffering from future climate change rather than to decrease it.

The IPCC Summaries for Policy Makers are the most widely read IPCC reports amongst politicians and non-scientists and are the basis for most climate change policy formulation. Yet these Summaries are prepared by a relatively small core writing team with the final drafts approved line-by-line by government representatives. The great majority of IPCC contributors and reviewers, and the tens of thousands of other scientists who are qualified to comment on these matters, are not involved in the preparation of these documents. The summaries therefore cannot properly be represented as a consensus view among experts.

Contrary to the impression left by the IPCC Summary reports:

- Recent observations of phenomena such as glacial retreats, sea-level rise and the migration of temperature-sensitive species are not evidence for abnormal climate change, for none of these changes has been shown to lie outside the bounds of known natural variability.

- The average rate of warming of 0.1 to 0.2 degrees Celsius per decade recorded by satellites during the late twentieth century falls within known natural rates of warming and cooling over the last 10,000 years.

- Leading scientists, including some senior IPCC representatives, acknowledge that today's computer models cannot predict climate. Consistent with this, and despite computer projections of temperature rises, there has been no net global warming since 1998. That the current temperature plateau follows a late twentieth century period of warming is consistent with the continuation today of natural multi-decadal or millennial climate cycling.

In stark contrast to the often repeated assertion that the science of climate change is 'settled', significant new peer-reviewed research has cast even more doubt on the hypothesis of dangerous human-caused global warming. But because IPCC working groups were generally instructed [15] to consider work published only through May, 2005, these important findings are not included in their reports; ie, the IPCC assessment reports are already materially outdated.

The UN climate conference in Bali has been planned to take the world along a path of severe CO_2 restrictions, ignoring the lessons apparent from the failure of the Kyoto Protocol, the chaotic nature of the European CO_2 trading market, and the ineffectiveness of other costly initiatives to curb greenhouse gas emissions. Balanced cost/benefit analyses provide no support for the introduction of global measures to cap and reduce energy consumption for the purpose of restricting CO_2 emissions. Furthermore, it is irrational to apply the 'precautionary principle' because many scientists recognize that both climatic coolings and warmings are realistic possibilities over the medium-term future.

The current UN focus on 'fighting climate change', as illustrated in the Nov. 27 UN Development Programme's Human Development Report, is distracting governments from adapting to the threat of inevitable natural climate changes, whatever forms they may take. National and international planning for such changes is needed, with a focus on helping our most vulnerable citizens adapt to conditions that lie ahead. Attempts to prevent global climate change from occurring are ultimately futile, and constitute a tragic misallocation of resources that would be better spent on humanity's real and pressing problems.

The arguments for and against global warming, and what to do about it, seem to oscillate like the pendulum of a grandfather clock. If scientists themselves can't agree, and accuse each other of being blinkered, it's small wonder the public is confused, and becoming less convinced by the year. In 2008, 47 per cent of American voters believed that human activity is the cause of global warming; a year later, the number was down to 39 per cent [16]. Let's forget the details about the accuracy or otherwise of Al Gore's projections. Let's also be quite clear that while temperature fluctuates up and down by the year [17], we are talking about long-term trends of 10 to 100 years, and about the average global temperature, not regional temperatures. The fact that the UK recently experienced three of the coldest winters on record (while Japan's winter was exceptionally mild in 2010) is neither here nor there. In any case, cold snaps in Western Europe may actually be due to climate change: melting ice from the arctic may negate the warming effects of the Gulf Stream. Remember that London is at the same latitude as the southern shore of Hudson Bay.

Even if we take the letter of the scientists to the Secretary-General of the UN, and the views of other sceptics, into account, it seems that most professional scientists do accept that global warming is occurring. They may disagree as to what measures should be taken to reduce it, and as to whether the rate of warming is accelerating, or not (Fig 4.1 – see page 80). They probably also accept that carbon dioxide levels in the atmosphere have been rising steadily for several centuries. These are now considerably higher than in 1750. As mentioned, the relationship between the two is reciprocal: global warming releases more CO_2 from the oceans (that constitute the main source on earth); increased CO_2 in the atmosphere leads to global warming through the greenhouse effect. It is a chicken and egg situation. There is good evidence that on occasions in the past, global warming led to higher levels of CO_2 in the atmosphere. Today, the evidence seems to point the other way (though mobile ocean fronts may reverse the trend somewhat [18]). The notion that gases like carbon dioxide and water vapour have a warming effect is not new: Svente Arrhenius, following earlier work by Jean Baptiste Joseph Fourier in France during the 1820s and by John Tyndall in England in 1863, showed it to be so in 1896 [19].

The IPCC says that the increase is anthropogenic: some 3% of CO_2 reaching the atmosphere is due to man (though that may prove to have been somewhat of an under-estimate [20]). Only 3%? Then why the fuss? The reason is that the carbon cycle between the atmosphere and the oceans (plus land) is very finely balanced [21]. Disturb it just a little, and the consequences can be huge. The question is what to do about it. One side recommends drastic cuts in carbon emissions: from power stations and the home [22], from automobiles and aeroplanes. Note that so far as the UK is concerned, its annual emission of CO_2 – just 2% of the total emitted by the world – is equal to the annual *increase* in CO_2 emission by China. The other side considers that the economic consequences of such measures are likely to be worse than accepting the inevitable.

They have a point. The Commission of the European Union (EU) is an unelected body of well-paid bureaucrats [23] who manage to produce some of the most hare-brained, economically flawed, schemes imaginable. In 2003 it issued a directive promoting the use of biofuels for transport, in order to reduce carbon emissions. If the UK were to follow the EU's recommendations, it would have to turn the *whole* of its farmland over to growing crops like corn, and still not have enough to meet its target – let alone having lost its entire cereal harvest for food. Moreover producing biofuels like ethanol (the alcohol we drink) is extremely inefficient: it actually uses *more* fossil fuels than it replaces. 'Filling a 4 x 4 with ethanol uses enough maize to feed a human for a year' [24]. The result has been nothing short of disastrous. As countries, many beyond the EU but persuaded by its edicts, turn arable land towards producing biofuels instead of edible crops like wheat and maize [25], the price of food is shooting up. Consumers in developed countries may be able to afford a near doubling in the price of such commodities,

Fig 4.1: Changes in northern hemisphere temperatures relative to the average value from 1961-90 in °C for the past 1,000 years. The different lines reflect data that come from different sources and methods, but all show the same dramatic increases in temperature in the last few decades. From P D Jones, T J Osborn and K R Briffa, 'The Evolution of Climate over the last Millennium', *Science* 292: 662-7 (2001) with permission

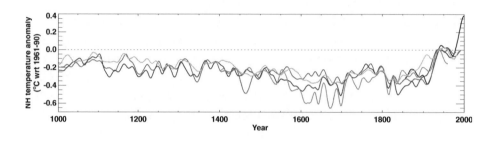

but those who live in the developing world can't [26]. Starvation stares them in the face. In any case, as to reducing 'carbon footprints' due to CO_2 emission, the production of biofuels sometimes does the opposite [27]. Thus do the actions of irresponsible and blinkered administrators threaten the lives of others.

Let us accept that the present warming is indeed due to man-made greenhouse gases [28]. How else, then, can we realistically reduce their emission into the atmosphere [29]? One way might be to improve the insulation in our houses. Almost half the amount of carbon dioxide released globally – and an equivalent share of world energy consumption – results from keeping buildings warm in winter and cool in summer, and lit up at all times. So far, most of the advances in 'green' housing have occurred at the individual level, as it is difficult to enforce at national levels. Then there is carbon capture: keep the power stations burning, but force the CO_2 that is discharged (whether from coal, natural gas or oil) down into the ground and away [30]. There is only one problem. It is hugely expensive: $100 per tonne of carbon dioxide avoided, with more than 7 billion tonnes emitted globally per year. The Chinese, though, seem able to capture carbon dioxide more cheaply [31]. Because gas-fired power stations emit less greenhouse gases than coal-fired ones, converting power stations from using coal to using gas has been suggested as one of the means to reduce emissions [32]. Greenhouse gas emission, incidentally, is not the only culprit. Soot particles from incomplete combustion in diesel engines, coal power plants, agricultural burning and wildfires, may account for as much as a third of today's global warming [33].

The best alternative to power stations that use fossil fuels owes its development not to a scientist but to a far-sighted US Admiral. Hyman G Rickover introduced nuclear-powered submarines to the navy, and the launch of Nautilus in 1954 showed that nuclear fission could be used to generate electricity safely and continuously. (Rickover was an eccentric commander. 'Piss me off' he would say when interviewing prospective entrants to his elite nuclear submarine training programme. In response, one young officer swept everything off the admiral's desk, including a rather fine replica of a sailing ship that was smashed to pieces when it hit the floor. The aspirant was accepted [34]). That year the USSR built the first nuclear power plant at Obrinsk. In the context of this chapter, the great advantage of nuclear fission is that it emits no CO_2 at all. Even the Greens are now admitting that nuclear power stations aren't as polluting and as dangerous as they once claimed. Note that the number of deaths to date from cancer after the Chernobyl disaster of 1986 is less than the *annual* death toll in Chinese coal mines. But building new power stations is also expensive. In the UK, we tried passing this to the French, who are better at it but now reluctant to invest [35]. If nuclear fusion (see Chapter 2) turns out to be feasible commercially, it could start to replace nuclear fission by mid-century. Combining the two processes in a hybrid reactor may solve the long-standing problem of radioactive waste [36]. Producing hydrogen by electrolysis of water, in order to heat your home, power cars and possibly aeroplanes, is another non-polluting, but expensive, source of energy [37]. These alternatives need to be developed irrespective of concerns about carbon emissions. Oil and gas reserves are likely to run out by 2100 [37a], and coal a century or so thereafter, though the latter may be too optimistic an estimate [38]. So quite apart from climate change, we will need to find alternative sources of energy. This is especially important in respect of the developing world, which is expanding its use of energy rapidly: at present most of the world's energy supplies are used by less than 20% of its population: a US citizen, for example, uses 50 times as much energy as a Bangladeshi.

What about 'renewables' [39] like wind and waves, tidal power and sunlight? It would be nice to think that the landscape of England will once more feature languidly turning wind-mills, as it did in Constable's day. But that is not what is intended. More than 7000 wind turbines on land and off shore [40], some as high as the Eiffel Tower, will not restore Britain to a rural idyll. Worse, it will not achieve the aim of providing a significant alternative to power stations [41] because wind is too unreliable: at peak demand, the output can be as little as 4% of maximum capability. The situation is no better in the USA: 10,000 wind turbines generate just 1% of its electricity, less than a single coal-fired power plant. Wind turbines are also extremely expensive to build and operate: power from nuclear energy is half as expensive as that from wind turbines, and that includes the cost of mining uranium and the decommissioning of outdated nuclear plants. Yet across Europe and the USA, the Green parties – whose members appear to lack economic sense and scientific insight in equal measure – continue to press for wind turbines at the expense of nuclear power. An alternative, as yet fanciful, idea is to harness the energy contained in the jet streams that circle the globe. This represents 'the highest concentration of renewable energy in large quantities' [42]. Designing a turbine that captures the wind at these high altitudes and somehow brings electricity down to earth is, of course, a huge challenge that has not yet been solved. Tides, unlike the wind on the earth's surface, never cease. The Portuguese were the first to build a wave farm, at Aguçadoura, and a tidal barrier across the Severn estuary in southern Britain may well generate a useful amount of electricity. Sunlight, despite its elusive rays in the northern hemisphere, can generate much of the electricity you use at home, but it's as unreliable as wind and it won't power your car (unless it's electric). In the south-west of the United States it's another story [43]. Let's not forget that the rays of the sun energised the emergence of plant life 1.5 billion years ago, and they have sustained all living organisms ever since. They could, in principle, maintain the entire energy requirements of the human race for years to come (Fig 4.2). All these measures come at a high cost [29], and all the time it's the taxpayer who foots the bill. That's whom the critics of focussing on CO_2 emissions have in mind, especially if he's sitting not in London or Los Angeles but in Lucknow or Lusaka.

During the mid-1990s, the Clinton administration in the USA hit on an ingenious way to restrict industrial sulphur dioxide (SO_2) emissions that were poisoning the countryside with acid rain. Each factory or power station was allocated an emission target. Above that amount, a tax was applied. Owners of installations that emitted less than this amount could sell their saving to the bigger polluters. It was essentially a 'cap and tax' scheme, and it worked extremely well: emissions dropped significantly [44]. It was probably inspired by a speech in January 1993 by the chair of the World Commission on Environment and Development, Norwegian Prime Minister Gro Harlem Brundtland (see Chapter 6), to the Forum on Technology and Governance on Capitol Hill. Brundtland recommended the use of carbon dioxide taxes and other economic sanctions to reduce the amount of fossil fuel used as energy. The government of New South Wales in Australia started a carbon dioxide 'cap and trade' scheme for electricity companies in 2003. The UK followed the next year, and soon the European Union made it mandatory for its members. As usual, the mandarins of Brussels got their figures wrong, but in principle the strategy is a good one, and

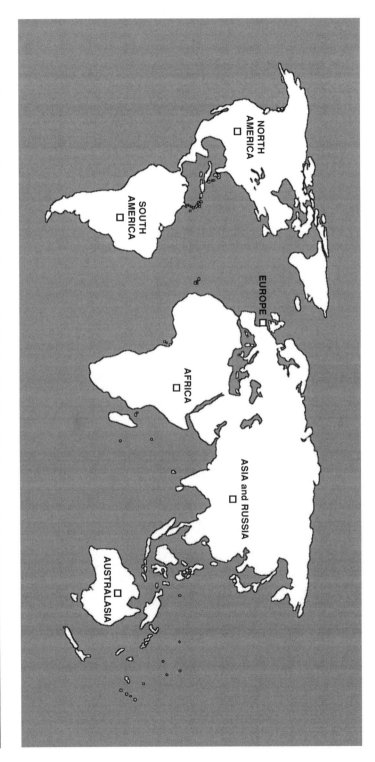

Fig 4.2: If the sunlight falling on each of the areas inside these six squares, each sited in an appropriate location, could be completely harvested, it would supply 50% more than the entire world's current energy needs. From *Powering the Planet*, the opening speech at the first annual California Clean Innovation Conference on May 11, 2007 at California Institute of Technology (Caltech) delivered by Dr Nathan S Lewis, George L. Argyros Professor of Chemistry at Caltech), with permission.

it is slowly being applied throughout the world. So far the amount of CO_2 traded falls well below the actual emissions. World-wide, 49 billion metric tons were emitted in 2004; just 1.6 billion metric tons were traded (in 2006, though the emissions had risen) [45]. It doesn't always work to the tax payer's advantage, either: in 2005 the UK government raised £21.9 billion in 'green taxes', such as air passenger duty, from the ordinary taxpayer. It put precisely half that into schemes to pay for 'carbon footprints'. And a proposed hike of £4 billion in car tax revenue will reduce vehicle emissions by less than 1%, according the UK Treasury's own figures [46]. However if you wish to pay for your carbon offset every time you fly – despite the fact that the IPCC 2001 report showed aviation to be of negligible consequence [47] – you are invited to contribute to an organisation called Climate Care [48]: a round trip from London to New York, for example, is costed at £13.52 for the 1.53 tonnes of carbon you will emit; if two of you fly, the cost is doubled (oh really?). Nigel Lawson likens such payments for one's carbon footprints to the sale of indulgences by the mediaeval church [49].

Deforestation is a major contributor to atmospheric CO_2 levels, since all green vegetation absorbs CO_2 [50]. If it weren't for the jungles of South America, Africa and Asia, and the forests of Canada and Russia, atmospheric CO_2 levels would be a lot higher than they are. Back in the 1980s, already, the entrepreneurial Jimmy Goldsmith [51] was telling Margaret Thatcher to tax British polluters and pass the money to Brazil, in exchange for an agreement not to cut down any more of the Amazonian rain forest [52]. He was right, and Brazil is promoting just such a scheme through the Amazon Fund [53]. Brazil may also be praised for meeting 30% of its demand for automobile fuel from ethanol derived from sugar cane, but it comes at the expense of swathes of virgin forest destroyed [54].

One of the foremost consequences of global warming, that affects the northern hemisphere more than the south, is the melting of the Arctic ice cap and the retreat of glaciers. Scientists emphasize the consequential rise in sea levels, but modern technology can surely do much to prevent the inundation of cities like New York and London, Mumbai and Shanghai, Tokyo and Manila. The Dutch have managed it for centuries. In any case, there will be plenty of time for populations to move away from threatened areas. So long as the few inhabitants of the Seychelles, the Maldives and the Andaman Islands are able to find a new home on the mainland, what matter if the islands are submerged? The tourists will just have to go to Mauritius instead. To my mind a more serious threat is posed by the melting snows of the Himalayas. This region feeds the largest rivers of Asia: Brahmaputra, Ganges, Indus, Mekong, Yangtse and Yellow River. A quartet of the world – 1.4 billion – rely on their waters for sustenance [55]. You will tell me that snow is nothing but rainfall, and that this is actually expected to increase in the northern hemisphere as warming continues. But rainfall over a wide region, where it simply drains into the ground or causes floods, is not the same as water running off a glacier along a well-formed river-bed. The Himalayas constitute a sink of frozen water that releases its contents in a gradual and beneficial way. I am reminded of the few days I spent in Ibadan, at the edge of rainforest in Nigeria. None of the taps in the guest house on campus gave forth water [56]. Nigeria's inability to conserve rain water (more than two decades ago) will, hopefully, be reversed by novel technology [57] yet to be developed in Asia. After all, the rivers that emanate from the Himalayas spawned two of the most inventive civilisations the world has ever seen. Let's hope they're up to the job today.

Another thought. If climate change is due to human activity [58], shouldn't we try to prevent the rise in global population, projected to exceed 9 billion by 2050? A group at the Optimum Population Trust in the UK has calculated that putting money into family planning over the next four decades is almost five times as effective – ie cheaper – than trying to reduce carbon dioxide emissions through 'green technology' [59].

How have the revelations in 2009 about questionable emails from scientists at the UK's Climatic Research Unit at the University of East Anglia in Norwich, the apparent mistakes about melting glaciers in the Himalayas, or the lack of evidence for diminishing crop yields in Africa, affected the overall conclusions? Not much. Continuously rising levels of carbon dioxide in the atmosphere over the last 250 years cannot be denied, and the relationship between greenhouse gases and temperature is also without question. Taking all the available evidence into account, it seems pretty clear that during that time, carbon dioxide has been the cause of increased global temperature, not the other way round. Variations in solar activity may also be contributing to global warming [60]. Estimating future temperatures is not an exact science, for sure, but that average temperatures across the globe are increasing – with blips in different areas and at different times (as mentioned, the winters of 2008, 2009 and 2010 were particularly cold in northern Europe) – is the most likely outcome during our lifetimes and that of our children and grand-children; local variations, and not just in temperature or carbon dioxide emissions, may be more important than previously recognised [61]. Long beyond the present century, we should be aware that as a result of long-term cyclical changes in the sun's activity, the earth is gradually moving out of the present inter-glacial period toward another ice age. That is likely to trump any man-made warming of our planet. But when it will happen is difficult to predict.

To conclude. The concentration of carbon dioxide in the atmosphere, and the average temperature on land and sea, are both increasing. How much of either is due to man remains to be established. How to prevent or respond to these developments is controversial. Politicians and scientists may be blinkered, but accepting climate change and paying for our carbon emissions is becoming as much a part of Western society (the mandarins of Cleveland and 700 scientists who remain sceptical about the IPCC's conclusions [62] excepted) as dumbing-down and single-sex marriages. Querying global warming is now as unacceptable as smoking or disparaging the EU. Which brings me to the next section.

Passive smoking
Nothing so well illustrates a blinkered attitude by scientists – their very evasion of facts – as the current ban on smoking. I am not referring to the damage caused to smokers. The evidence is clear. In 1950 two British statisticians, Richard Doll and Austin Bradford Hill, found that of 649 men and 60 women suffering from carcinoma of the lung, 647 of the men and 41 of the women had been smokers. By 1956 they had extended the risks of smoking to heart disease and other fatal ailments. Long-term smoking, they concluded, can shorten life span by 10 years. Gradually doctors, politicians, the public – all save members of the tobacco industry [63] – got the message. The level of smoking soon declined across the Western world. Only in communist-controlled eastern Europe and China, as well as in other depressed parts of the world, did the harassed and dispossessed populace continue to derive a bit of pleasure from the puff of a cheap cigarette. As some men in a West African village put it to a colleague of mine when she asked them whether they were aware of the link between smoking and cancer, 'Yes, they were aware of the dangers, but felt that cancer of the lung is a disease of older people, and that they were more likely to die of malaria or dysentery by the time they were 50. For them, smoking cigarettes was one of the few pleasures that they had in life' [64]. There is, however, no doubt in anyone's mind that smokers should be vigorously encouraged to drop the habit, and non-smokers – especially children – discouraged from taking it up.

Now scientists are successfully pressing for governments to ban smoking in public places, so that non-smokers are not exposed to 'secondhand smoke' or 'environmental tobacco smoke (ETS)'. As of 2007, you were not allowed to light up in Argentina, Australia, Bhutan, California (not the entire US as yet), Denmark, Finland, Hong Kong, Iceland, Ireland, Italy, Lithuania, Netherlands, New Zealand, Norway, Portugal, Sweden, Thailand, UK and Uruguay. The ban applies to hotels and restaurants [65], trains and buses, offices and shopping malls. Even outdoors: California's sunny beaches have become 'no smoking' zones. In 1959, already, the American Cancer Society had commissioned an extensive study into the hazards of second-hand smoking. The lead scientists on the project, James Enstrom and Geoffrey Kabat, monitored the health of 118,094 Californians. This included 35,561 non-smokers who were married to smokers. 40 years later Enstrom and Kabat had completed the project and submitted their paper for publication. Their conclusion was that 'there is no causal relation between environmental tobacco smoke and tobacco-related mortality'.

The American Cancer Society was dismayed. This was not the outcome they had expected. They withdrew funding and aborted the project. Enstrom and Kabat nevertheless decided to publish their result. No scientific journal in the USA would touch their paper, though acceptability is judged by an editorial board of scientists. In the end the *British Medical Journal* decided to give their findings the airing that the authors rightfully felt was due to them. They toned down their conclusions somewhat: 'The results do not support a causal relation between environmental tobacco smoke and tobacco related mortality, although they do not rule out a small effect. The association between exposure to environmental tobacco smoke and coronary heart disease and lung cancer may be considerably weaker than believed.' Politicians, anti-smoking campaigners and many supposedly objective scientists, were outraged and tried to have the *British Medical Journal* article retracted. In fairness to them, the findings of a survey conducted by the Japanese National Cancer Center Research Institute [66] seemed to support their case.

In the meantime the US Surgeon General and the US National Research Council had each published a report on the subject. Both had come to the conclusion that the evidence for an association between passive smoking and coronary heart disease 'was inconclusive' [67]. The US Environmental Protection Agency (EPA) now entered the fray. Determined to prove a link, it published a report based largely on estimated figures, without statistical back-up. It came up with the finding that in the US environmental tobacco smoke caused 3,000 cancer deaths per year, that 150,000 to 300,000 cases annually of lower respiratory tract illness in infants and children are due to ETS, and that more than 5,000 infants die of sudden infant death syndrome (SIDS), or cot deaths (see Chapter 2) every year. The latter cause, the EPA claimed, was directly attributable to maternal smoking [68]. None of these assertions have been corroborated by properly conducted epidemiological surveys.

One such study had, however, been commissioned by the World Health Organisation (WHO) together with the International Agency for Research on Cancer (IARC), in the late 1980s. A consortium of epidemiologists and cancer specialists set out to compare 650 lung cancer patients with 1,650 healthy people from seven European countries. The survey included non-smokers who were married to smokers or worked with smokers, non-smokers who both worked with and were married to smokers, and non-smokers who had grown up with smokers. It found that there was no 'statistically significant' risk to non-smokers, either at home or at work. What did the WHO do? It ignored the findings of the very study it had set up ten years previously. How, then, do we know about this? Because on this occasion the media got it right. They exposed the biased malice of the establishment against a perfectly legitimate scientific finding [69].

Such evasion of scientific findings is rare in Western medicine. In the Soviet Union (USSR) during Stalin's time, it was another matter. Trofim Denisovich Lysenko was a biologist who believed in the Lamarckian idea that the environment in which a plant or an animal finds itself, affects not only its own life, but leaves a mark on subsequent generations as well. This view is in contrast to that espoused by Alfred Russell Wallace and Charles Darwin, and shown over and over again to be correct: the environment does *not* affect the progeny of an organism exposed to a particular climatic condition. High altitude climbers can slowly adapt to low oxygen levels in a number of ways, but their children will not be born with this facility [70]. On the other hand those who have lived at high altitudes for many generations are able to tolerate the thin air from birth onwards. The inhabitants of the high Andes, for example, counter low oxygen tension by producing more haemoglobin – the protein that carries oxygen around the body – in their red blood cells. This is because tens of thousands of years ago a chance mutation (see the next chapter for details) occurred in an individual that enabled that person to make more haemoglobin and hence to be able to tolerate low oxygen levels better. This advantageous attribute then gradually spread across the group of high altitude dwellers through mating. Their resistance to low oxygen levels meant that they began to out-breed their less fortunate contemporaries. What I have described is an example of the way evolution works by natural selection.

To return to Lysenko. His work during the 1930s appeared to show (at least to him) that wheat grown in a cold climate produces seeds that are then able to withstand the arctic Siberian weather better than others: the memory of harsh conditions is retained in their progeny. The result of putting these ideas into practice failed miserably, and millions of Russians starved to death. Stalin, however, liked the concept because it implied that people brought up under Marxism produced Marxist offspring. Lysenko became Director of the Institute of Genetics and President of the V I Lenin All-Union Academy of Agricultural Sciences. The evolutionary ideas of Wallace and Darwin were proscribed in the same way that the Copernican view of heliocentricity was forbidden by the Church of Rome in the sixteenth century. Lysenko's views persevered. When I was invited by the Academy of Sciences to give some lectures in Russia during the late 1980s, my hosts told me that at least two generations of Russian students – from the 1940s until the introduction of *glasnost* and *perestroika* by Mikhail Gorbachev – had been officially blinkered to the facts of evolution, and biological research was only now beginning to catch up with that outside the former Soviet Union.

I appreciate that living in smoke-filled rooms can be extremely unpleasant for non-smokers (personally I enjoy the aroma of cigars so much that I tend to follow a cigar smoker in the street like a bloodhound). Before the invention of deodorants, crowded places in hot countries could be pretty nauseating too, but it did not damage your health either. The irony of the determination by scientists – not to mention politicians and administrators – to stick to preconceived ideas that are at odds with the findings of properly conducted research, is that one of the most respected epidemiologists in the world, a man who for half a century campaigned for a ban on smoking, remarked that so far as he was concerned, 'The effects of other people smoking in my presence is so small it doesn't worry me' [71]. And a year after the no-smoking legislation was adopted in England, the number of emergency admissions for myocardial infarction had dropped by just 2% [72]. Nevertheless there is now talk of extending the ban to smoking *in parks*.

Folk medicine

Until the late nineteenth century, there was only folk medicine in the world. Whether you lived in a sophisticated metropolis like Paris, London, St Petersburg or New York, in a vibrant city like Calcutta, Shanghai, Cairo or Buenos Aires, in a village deep in the forests of Borneo, Madagascar, Mexico or Brazil, you had to rely pretty much on herbal medicines. The hygiene may have been better in Boston than in Bangkok, the surgery cleverer – though still without anaesthetic – in Vienna than in Varanasi, but there was little you could do anywhere about an infected finger or a fever, about consumption (tuberculosis) or incessant diarrhoea. Sitting it out (literally) was the only option [73]. Not until the discovery of antiseptics and anaesthetics at the dawn of the twentieth century, and of antibiotics 50 years later, did Western medicine become effective. The circulation of the heart may have been discovered four hundred years earlier, but the sole remedy for a failing heart was to swallow a concoction made from foxgloves [74]. Even today, when science and technology are advancing so rapidly, it is sobering to acknowledge that half a century after the structure of DNA was revealed, genetic therapy in humans is still an unrealised goal. And over 95% of pain killers in use today are based on derivates of aspirin (from the bark of the willow tree) and opium (from poppies) [75].

What has all this to do with blinkered scientists? Their refusal to give credence to the two oldest medical systems in the world: Indian Ayurvedic and Chinese Traditional Medicine. In the same way that arrogant atheists deny the benefits of religious beliefs that have been held by billions of people over thousands of years (see Chapter 5), so Western scientists reject the notion that folk medicine, as practised in India and China for as long a time, has any rational foundation. If this book results in nothing more than reminding members of my profession that practices which have survived trial and error over millennia should be taken seriously, I will have achieved one of my aims. It is true that the tenets of Ayurveda and of Chinese traditional medicine have no obvious consonance with biochemistry and physiology, that the therapies they prescribe have not been assessed by 'double blind' studies [76]. But that does not mean that we should regard them to be as worthless as the homeopathic law of infinite dilution.

The basis of Ayurvedic practice is to allocate human characteristics like physique, skin texture, hair, nails, appetite, food habits, bowels, digestion rate, movements and mental nature to three categories or *Prakriti*. You tend to be either more of a *Vata*, a *Pitta*, or a *Kapha*. Of course there is much overlap between the three categories, but that is only to be expected. The most precise way that we in the West have of classifying individuals is by analysis of the type of protein – known as HLA or human leucocyte antigen – present on the surface of our lymphocytes or white cells. HLA-bearing lymphocytes play an important role in immune mechanisms such as the ability to accept an organ from another person, and in the susceptibility to different diseases. Any one person will have a mix of the HLA proteins, so 'One individual differs from all others not because he has unique endowments but because he has a unique *combination* of endowments' [77]. A recent comparison between the HLA status and the *Prakriti* category of 76 individuals has concluded that there is 'a reasonable correlation between HLA alleles (types) and *Prakriti* type' [78]. I have to admit that the number of people tested, and the correlation between *Prakriti* type and HLA status is pretty weak, but at least the study is a first attempt to analyse Ayurvedic categories by scientific criteria. If there is indeed an explanation for the different *Prakriti* types in terms of the HLA system, it will give Ayurvedic classifications a reality not granted to them before.

Another approach has been to look at various biochemical parameters such as liver function tests and lipid (fat) profiles, as well as the expression of certain genes, in the three *Prakriti* groups [79]. The authors claim significant differences between *Vata*, *Pitta*, and *Kapha* types. Like the HLA study, it is no more than a hint that differences between the three groups might be capable of definition according to scientific criteria. Such approaches to Ayurvedic medicine, of course, do not give credence to some of its remedies. These include purgatives and laxatives, bloodletting and enemas, herbal preparations and yoga. Apart from the latter, all were in use in Europe over a period of time almost as long as Ayurvedic practices in India, and some – like bloodletting – are as lethal. Others have proved beneficial because the treatment works as a placebo (see next chapter). In some cases, though, an Ayurvedic remedy can be as effective as a 'Western' procedure. Take lymphatic filariasis.

This disease is characterised by the swelling (oedema) of a part of the body, like a leg, to such enormous proportions that the term elephantiasis has been applied. The cause of the swelling is the presence of tiny threadlike worms, generally absorbed through the bite of a mosquito, that block lymphatic capillaries. Normally the flow of lymph (a watery liquid distinct from blood) helps to maintain the right amount of fluid within the body's organs. When a particular lymphatic vessel is blocked, the respective organ retains water and swells. Some 2.5 million people in India suffer from lymphatic filariasis, with almost half the entire population at risk. Surgery and related operations can generally reduce a swollen limb, but the cost is beyond the means of most patients. A fairly complicated Ayurvedic alternative consists of treatment with herbs, breathing exercises, yoga, and other measures. A recent study has followed this form of therapy among sufferers in various parts of India [80]. When you witness an elephantine sized leg gradually shrink to normal size, there can be little doubt about the efficacy of the procedure.

An attempt to correlate the HLA profile of 706 people with their status as defined by Traditional Chinese Medicine (TCM), namely properties such as blood flow, pulse, heartbeat, facial appearance and body figure, has led to a conclusion similar to that for Ayurveda: 'Our initial results indicated that some HLA alleles and serological types associate with certain TCM constitutions. This suggests a genetic basis for the classification of physical constitution in TCM. This study lays the foundation for future in-depth studies into the theory of this type of ancient medicine using modern biological approaches' [81]. Again, the correlation is not that strong, but if the association proves to be correct, it will put Traditional Chinese Medicine on a new footing. Another way of trying to give scientific credence to Chinese, as well as to Japanese and Korean, traditional medical classifications is to explain them in terms of systems biology [82]. The fact that acupuncture may, in some instances, work better than a carefully designed placebo [76], and that two thousand years ago it was the Chinese who discovered the beneficial effects of *Artemesia annua*, now the prophylactic of choice against malaria in the Western world, surely attests to their ingenuity and skill in medicine [82a].

This chapter has introduced a note of caution. Scientists themselves are sometimes blinkered and susceptible to pre-conceived ideas, as I have shown in regard to climate change, passive smoking and folk medicine. But then it's often difficult for the best of them to predict future developments. I once asked a colleague (a Nobel laureate), in connection with a book I was editing [83], what he thought would be the key advances in his field over the next decade: 'I am an experimental scientist, Charles, not a star-gazer', he replied.

It's true! A hundred and fifty years ago, the journal *Scientific American* published the following remark. 'We believe that no particular use is made of the fluid petroleum, from the "tar springs" of California, except as a lotion for bruises and rheumatic affections ...' [84]. With the benefit of hindsight, this may be considered the most blinkered scientific comment of the nineteenth century. It is matched only by three remarks made during the twentieth century. In 1933, the 'father of nuclear physics', expressed the view that harnessing nuclear energy was 'moonshine'; this prediction of Ernest Rutherford's was 'the only major bloomer in scientific judgement Rutherford ever made' [85]. Ten years later, Thomas Watson, Chairman of IBM, said 'I think there is a world market for maybe five computers' [86]. Returning to petroleum, there is the prognosis made by T E Lawrence (Lawrence of Arabia) during the 1920s. The writer Robert Graves was visiting the former soldier in his rooms at All Souls College in Oxford. These contained two fine chairs, which had been presented to Lawrence in gratitude for his response to a question. 'An American oil-financier had come in suddenly one day when I was there and said: "I am here from the States, Colonel Lawrence, to ask a single question. You are the only man who will answer it honestly. Do Middle-Eastern conditions justify my putting any money in South Arabian oil?" Lawrence, without rising, quietly answered: "No." 'That's all I wanted to know; it was worth coming for. Thank you, and good day' [87].

Notes

[1]   Goddard Institute for Space Studies at Columbia University in New York

[2]   Urban 'islands' are warmer than the surrounding countryside

[3]   See http://www.dailytech.com/article.aspx?newsid=10866

[4]   US National Oceanic and Atmospheric Administration; see University of Illinois website The Cryosphere Today: http://arctic.atmos.uiuc.edu/ cryosphere/. For a broader view, see Alexandra Witze: Losing Greenland. *Nature* 452: 798-802 (2008)

[5]   See André Bornemann *et al*: Isotopic evidence for glaciation during the cretaceous supergreenhouse. *Science* 319: 189-192 (2008)

[6]   See http://royalsociety.org/displaypagedoc.asp?id=20742

[7]   Al Gore:*An inconvenient truth. The planetary emergency of global warming and what you can do about it* (Bloomsbury, London, 2006)

[8]   From the diary of Gunnar Jahn, chairman of the Nobel Peace Prize committee; quoted by Stanley Wolpert: *Gandhi's Passion. The Life and Legacy of Mahatma Gandhi* (Oxford University Press, 2001), p 265

[9]   Tom Nuttall: In fact. From the pages of *Prospect* magazine (Preface Publishing, London, 2008), p 11

[10]   See http://cei.org/pdf/5820.pdf

[11]   The evidence from Russia's Vostock station in Antarctica is compelling. Ice cores, that reveal annual atmospheric CO_2 levels going back 400,000 years, show that CO_2 levels are now higher than they have ever been over that time. For details, see, eg, Gabrielle Walker and Sir David King: *The Hot Topic. How to tackle global warming and still keep the lights on* (Bloomsbury, London, 2008), p 21

[12]   See http://www.ipcc.ch/pdf/assessment-report/ar4/syr/ar4_syr_frontmatter.pdf

[13]   John Christy, Professor of Atmospheric Science at the University of Alabama; reported on BBC News 13 Nov 2007 as 'No consensus of IPCC's level of ignorance'; see John Christy: My Nobel Moment, *Wall Street Journal* Nov 1, 2007

[14]   'Errors covertly corrected by the IPCC after publication' by Lord Monckton of Brenchley, March, 2007, Center for Science and Public Policy, Washington, DC; www.scienceandpolicy.org

[15]   See http://ipcc-wg1.ucar.edu/wg1/docs/wg1_timetable_2006-08-14.pdf

[16]   David Appell: Stumbling over data. *Scientific American* 301: Aug 2009, p 12

[17]   Seasonal rises in one hemisphere are generally cancelled out by falls in the other hemisphere

[18]   Rainer Zahn: Beyond the CO_2 connection. *Nature* 460: 335-336, 2009

[19]   Svante Arrhenius: *On the Influence of Carbonic Acid in the Air upon the Temperature of the Ground*, London, Edinburgh, and Dublin Philosophical Magazine and Journal of Science (fifth series), April 1896. vol 41, pages 237–275

[20]   Richard Monastersky: A burden beyond bearing. *Nature* 458: 1091-1094, 2009

[21]   See, for example, John B Miller: Sources, sinks and seasons. *Nature* 451: 26-27, 2008

[22]   Better insulation and more energy-efficient lighting alone can reduce the emission of CO_2 from buildings by more than 50%

[23]   The annual audits of the commission have not been signed off for the past sixteen years because of alleged irregularities

[24]   Mary Riddell in the UK *Daily Telegraph*, Apr 24, 2008. But scientists are working on ways that use microbes to turn the cellulose (that humans cannot digest) of plants into ethanol, with much less environmental damage and lower energy expenditure, and even using microbes themselves as source of ethanol

[25]   There are much better solutions. Jatropha, a shrub that produces oily seeds ideal for biodiesel, grows well in the hot, dry regions of India and sub-Saharan Africa. It should replace the use of corn or sugarcane (for ethanol) and palm oil (for diesel). See, eg, Rebecca Renner: Green Gold in a Shrub, *Scientific American* 296, June 2007, pp 9-10, Daemon Fairless: The little shrub that could – maybe, *Nature* 449: 652-655, 2007 and Jeff Tollefson: Not your father's biofuels, *Nature* 451: 880-883, 2008 and Judy D Wall, Caroline S Harwood and Arnold Demain (eds): *Bioenergy* (ASM Press, 2008), but note also some recent reservations over Jatropha's potential, as expressed by Katharine Sanderson: Wonder weed plans fail to flourish, *Nature* 461: 328-329, 2009. For a recent survey of biofuel use, see *Nature* 474: S1-S30, 2011

[26] The poorest households in the US spend 16% of their budget on food (in the case of the wealthy, the percentage is even lower); in Indonesia, however, it is 50%, in Vietnam 65% and in Nigeria 73%: *International Herald Tribune*, April 11, 2008

[27] See Jörn P W Scharlemann and William F Laurance: How green are biofuels? *Science* 319: 43-44 (2008)

[28] These comprise carbon dioxide, methane (of which a single cow exhales some 280 litres a day [9]), nitrous oxide and halocarbons. Water vapour is actually the strongest greenhouse gas, but only 0.001% of it is man-made and for this and other reasons its contribution is generally ignored. So far as carbon dioxide is concerned, a colleague tells me that according to his calculations, at least 80% of man-made CO_2 comes not from burning fossil fuels but from the oceans: it is released by the vortex created at the stern of large ships. This results in the CO_2 being forced up from lower depths (where most of it resides). Since the boats are largely oil-transporting tankers, the blame is the same. But the remedy is different: instead of spending the money on carbon capture, the funds should be used towards constructing better ships

[29] An admirable review that compares the efficacy of different ways of generating 'Electricity without carbon' is to be found in *Nature* 454: 816-823, 2008; see also the excellent book by David J C MacKay: *Sustainable Energy – without the hot air*. (CIT, Cambridge, 2008; available free at www.withouthotair.com), as well as Ahmed F Zobaa and Ramesh Bansal (eds): *Handbook of Renewable Energy Technology* (World Scientific, Singapore/Imperial College Press, London, 2010)

[30] See, eg, Quirin Schiermeier: Putting the carbon back. The hundred billon tonne challenge, *Nature* 442: 620-623, 2006; the OIBC Report 2008 on *Alternative energy, health and the environment*: http://www.oibc.org.uk/OIBC%20report%20(final%20and%20complete).doc; and Nicola Jones: Sucking it up, *Nature* 458: 1094-1097, 2009

[31] Jeff Tollefson: Low-cost carbon-capture project sparks interest. *Nature* 469: 276-277, 2011

[32] See Walker and King p 102, note 11, above

[33] Jeff Tollefson: Climate's smoky spectre. *Nature* 460: 29-32, 2009

[34] A good biography of this inspired man is by Norman Polmar and Thomas
      B Allen: *Rickover: Controversy and Genius* (Simon & Schuster, NY, 1982)

[35] 80% of electricity in France is generated by nuclear power

[36] Ed Gerstner: The hybrid returns. *Nature* 460: 25-28 (2009)

[37] Ulrich Bossel, a German scientist, promoted this strongly in 2003
      [Hydrogen Economy Report 2003] but seems to have changed his mind
      somewhat subsequently: www.efcf.com/reports, which is not surprising,
      given that Nobel Laureate Burton Richter considers that 'Hydrogen fuel
      cells are losers'. But see Louis Schlapbach: Hydrogen-fuelled vehicles.
      Nature 460: 809-811, 2009 and Jeff Tollefson: Fuel of the future? *Nature*
      464: 1262-1264, 2010

[37a] And the cost is becoming unsustainable. See James Murray and David
      King: Oil's tipping point has passed. *Nature* 481: 433-435, 2012

[38] Richard Heinberg and David Fridley: The end of cheap coal. *Nature* 468:
      367-369, 2010

[39] I've always found this word as meaningless as 'organic' applied to food.
      Nothing is renewed: surely 'inexhaustibles' or 'sustainables' is what is meant

[40] To follow the EU's directive, the number should be 20,000, not 7,000

[41] According to the EU, renewables are supposed to provide 10% of Britain's
      electricity by 2010, 20% by 2020; currently they contribute 1%, of which
      half comes from wind. Nevertheless, the UK government has decided to
      subsidise the wind turbine industry by £0.5 billion (of tax-payers money):
      Daily Telegraph August 31 2007

[42] Erik Vance: High hopes. *Nature* 460: 564-566, 2009

[43] Ken Zweibel, James Mason and Vasilis Fthenakis: By 2050 solar power
      could end US dependence on foreign oil and slash greenhouse gas
      emissions. *Scientific American*: 298: January 2008, pp 48-57. See also

Richard Cohen: *Chasing the Sun. The Epic Story of the Star That Gives Us Life* (Simon and Schuster, London, 2010), especially pp 385-407

[44]   See Walker and King, pp 166-176, note 11 above

[45]   David G Victor and Danny Cullenward: Making carbon markets work, *Scientific American* 297: Dec 2007, pp 44-5; also A Danny Ellerman and others: *Pricing Carbon: The European Union Emissions Trading Scheme* (Cambridge University Press, 2010)

[46]   *Daily Telegraph* Apr 24, 2008

[47]   See Climate Change 2001: The scientific basis, published for the IPCC by Cambridge University Press, p 37

[48]   See www.climatecare.org

[49]   Nigel Lawson: *An Appeal to Reason: A Cool Look at Global Warming* (Duckworth Overlook, London, 2008), p 78

[50]   Preventing forest fires might seem a step in the right direction, but in fact it is not. See Keren Blankfeld Schultz: The Puzzling Inferno. *Scientific American* 299: Aug 2008, pp 17-18

[51]   Sir James was younger brother of Edward Goldsmith, the founder of the ecology movement in the UK

[52]   World-wide, the destruction of tropical rain forest has not slowed. 27 million hectares – 2.4% of the total rain forest – was lost between 2000 and 2005, the same as in the 1990s: *Nature* 454: 140 (2008)

[53]   Jeff Tollefson: Paying to save the rainforests. *Nature* 460: 936-937 (2009)

[54]   Though the government itself is trying to curtail this: see, eg, Jeff Tollefson: Brazil goes to was against logging. *Nature* 452: 134-137 (2008)

[55]   See also Jane Qiu: The Third Pole. *Nature* 454: 393-396 (2008) but these glaciers appear to be more stable than previously thought; see Jonathan Bamber: Shrinking glaciers under scrutiny, *Nature* 482: 482-483 (2012)

[56]   The International Institute of Tropical Agriculture, down the road, had no
       such problems. Its water tower harvested rainwater perfectly. One suspects
       that local difficulties (aka corruption) had more to do with water
       conservation than technological problems

[57]   They'll also have to do something about industrial pollution: 70% of
       China's rivers and lakes are so contaminated that their water can't even be
       used for irrigation, let alone drinking; see David Smith: *The Dragon and
       the Elephant. China, India and the New World Order* (Profile Books,
       London, 2007; paperback 2008), p 201

[58]   There is no dearth of publications on the topic of climate change: in
       addition to that by Walker and King and that by Nigel Lawson, both
       published in 2008, the previous year had seen Kerry Emanuel: *What We
       Know About Climate Change* (MIT Press, Cambridge MA, 2007), and
       Joseph F C DiMento and Pamela Doughman (eds) *Climate Change: What
       it means for Us, Our Children and Our Grandchildren* (MIT Press,
       Cambridge MA, 2007). In 2009 at least five major books were published:
       four of these are fairly partisan, one is more measured. Three of the
       partisan books are on the side of global warming [Al Gore: *Our Choice: A
       Plan to Solve the Climate Crisis* (Rodale Books, 2009); James Hansen:
       *Storms of My Grandchildren: The Truth About the Coming Climate
       Catastrophe and Our Last Chance to Save Humanity* (Bloomsbury USA,
       2009); Stephen H Schneider: *Science as a Contact Sport: Inside the Battle
       to Save Earth's Climate* (National Geographic Society, 2009)]; the other is
       against [Christopher Booker: *The Real Global Warming Disaster*
       (Continuum, London, 2009)]. A more balanced view may be obtained
       from Dieter Helm and Cameron Hepburn (eds): *The Economics and
       Politics of Climate Change* (Oxford University Press, 2009). So far, 2010
       has seen four books, each acknowledging climate change, but offering
       different solutions: Stewart Brand: *Whole Earth Discipline: An
       Ecopragmatist Manifesto* (Viking/Atlantic, 2009/2010), Bill McKibben:
       Earth: Making a Life on a Tough New Planet (Times Books, 2010), Paul
       N Edwards: *A Vast Machine: Computer Models, Climate Data, and the
       Politics of Global Warming* (MIT Press, Cambridge MA, 2010) and Roger
       Pielke, Jr: *The Climate Fix: What Scientists and Politicians Won't Tell You
       About Global Warming* (Basic Books, New York, 2010). And then there's
       Richard Cohen, op cit, pp 545-563, note 43 above. But Nathan Lewis'

excellent   talk   (http://nsl.caltech.edu/   _detail/energy:energy.
engsci.png?id=energy) at the first annual California Clean Innovation
Conference in 2007 takes a lot of beating

[59] *Fewer Emitters, Lower Emissions, Less Cost*; see www.optimum
population.org/reducingemissions.pdf

[60] See, for example, Richard Cohen, op cit, pp 545-563, note 43 above

[61] Tim Lenton: 2^0C or not 2^0C? That is the climate question. *Nature* 473: 7
(2011)

[62] US Senate Minority Report: more than 700 international scientists dissent
over man-made global warming claims. Scientists continue to debunk
'consensus' in 2008 and 2009: http://epw.senate.gov/public/index.cfm?
FuseAction=Files.View&FileStore_id=83947f5d-d84a-4a84-ad5d-6e2d71
db52d9

[63] See, for example, David Michaels: *Doubt is Their Product: How Industry's
Assault on Science Threatens Your Health* (Oxford University Press, 2008)

[64] From Charles Pasternak: *Quest: The Essence of Humanity* (Wiley,
Chichester, 2003) p 312

[65] Only in a Spanish restaurant did I see a notice which read: '*Se no prohibe
fumar*': smoking allowed. That was in 2007; by the following year, the
notice had disappeared

[66] R N Proctor: *Cancer wars: How politics shapes what we know and don't
know about cancer* (Basic Books, New York, 1996) p 107

[67] US DHHS,1989 'Environmental tobacco smoke: measuring exposures and
assessing health effects', US National Research Council, 1986

[68] 'Respiratory health effects of passive smoking: lung cancer and other
disorders', funded by the Indoor Air Division, Office of Atmosphere and
Indoor Air Programs, Office of Health and Environmental Assessment,
Office of Research and Development, EPA, December 1992

[69] Victoria Macdonald: 'Passive smoking doesn't cause cancer – official'. *Sunday Telegraph*, March 8, 1998

[70] See http://news.nationalgeographic.com/news/2004/02/0224_040225_evolution_2.html

[71] Sir Richard Doll on *Desert Island Discs*, BBC Radio 4, February 23, 2001

[72] Michelle Sims *et al*: Short term impact of smoke-free legislation in England: retrospective analysis of hospital admissions for myocardial infarction. *BMJ*: 340 c2161 (2010)

[73] Actually the latter could easily have been halted by a simple technology: a double ended-spoon that contains glucose in one recess, salt in the other. Swallowing the powders reverses the flow of fluid across the intestine, but our forebears were ignorant of this simple physiological process

[74] So effective, however, is digitalis that – together with other measures – it is still in use today

[75] P D Wall: Pain: *The Science of Suffering* (Weidenfeld & Nicolson, London, 1999) p 114

[76] See Simon Singh and Edzard Ernst: *Trick or Treatment? Alternative Medicine on Trial* (Bantam Press, London, 2008)

[77] Peter Medawar: *The Uniqueness of the Individual* (2nd edn, Dover Publications, New York, 1981), p 134

[78] Patwardhan Bhushan, Joshi Kalpana and Chopra Arvind: Classification of Human population based on HLA gene polymorphism and the Concept of *Prakriti* in Ayurveda. *J Alternative and Complementary Med* 11: 349-353 (2005)

[79] B Prasher et al: Whole genome expression and biochemical correlates of extreme constitutional types defined in Ayurveda. *J Transl Med* 6: 48 (2008)

[80] S R Narahar, T J Ryan, E Mahadevan, K S Bose and K S Prasanna: Management of filarial lymphoedema for rural communities. *Lymphology* 40: 3-13 (2007)

[81] Shangwu Chen *et al*: HLA class II polymorphisms associated with the physiologic characteristics defined by traditional chinese medicine: linking modern genetics with an ancient medicine. *J Alternative and Complementary Med* 13: 231-239 (2007)

[82] See Denis Noble: *The Music of Life. Biology beyond genes* (OUP, 2006; paperback 2008), despite some obvious difficulties: Jane Qiu: A culture in balance. *Nature* 448: 126-128, 2007

[82a] Traditional Asian Medicine. An ancient practice in modern times. *Nature* 480: S81-103 (2011)

[83] Biosciences 2000. *Current Aspects and Prospects for the Next Millennium* (Imperial College Press, 1999)

[84] Quoted in *Scientific American* 296: May 2007, p 7

[85] C P Snow: *The Two Cultures and the Scientific Revolution. The Rede Lecture, 1959* (Cambridge University Press, Cambridge, 1959), p 31

[86] Quoted by Denis Noble, p 55 (note 82, above)

[87] Robert Graves: *Goodbye to all that* (first published by Jonathan Cape, 1929; The Folio Society, London, 1981), p 258

CHAPTER 5

Religious belief: arrogance and ignorance

MY visit to the Taj Mahal some years ago left me with an indelible memory. I was attending a rather boring scientific congress in New Delhi, and jumped at the opportunity to spend a day away from the stuffy lecture rooms. The long bus ride was tedious and depressing. Though sitting comfortably in a reasonably clean and mechanically sound coach laid on by the organisers, looking out, village after village, at the families living in squalor by the side of the road brought home the reality that India is truly a place of two nations, of 'the rich and the poor', as Disraeli said of England in 1845 [1]. In New Delhi I had taken tea with the aged sister of the Maharaja of Baroda. Now I was passing families whose home was a discarded flood-water pipe, a make-shift hovel of sacking with a corrugated iron sheet filched from a scrap yard, or simply the underneath of an abandoned truck. Cows were defecating among the naked toddlers playing in the dirt, and *Taenia saginata* (tape worm), *Vibrio cholera*, and measles virus were multiplying unseen within their human hosts. Eventually we reached Agra. After a brief visit to the Red Fort, that once housed the Peacock Throne on which successive Mughal emperors had sat until its removal to Persia by an invading army in 1739, we worked our way through the seething crowd of sellers of post-cards, miniature Taj Mahals, bracelets and necklaces of 'gold' and 'silver', 'amber' and 'jade', bottles of Coca Cola, and coconuts sliced open in your presence (that provide the safest of any drink in India). Past dozens of tall Scandinavians in shorts and short Thais in shiny leg-wear (the Japanese do not visit India: it is too dirty for them) looking for their respective tour-guides, we went on. Down another side street, and there it stood before our eyes. I was back in the realm of the rich: of a ruler whose wealth outshone by far that of his near contemporary the Sun King of France.

The shrine built by the emperor Shah Jahan in memory of his beloved wife Mumtaz Mahal (hence Taj Mahal), who died in childbirth (it was her 14th) in 1631, justifies every visitor's expectation. It took 20,000 labourers 16 years to erect it, and is as much a reminder of the ingenuity and tenacity of man as the great pyramid of Gizeh or the temple of Kukalkan [2] in Chichen Itza. My visit, however, was particularly memorable not on account of the beauty of the place. Rather it was a conversation with a fellow delegate from the conference. We were walking around the back of the Taj Mahal, gazing at the Jumna (Yamuna) river winding its way below us. My companion, a serious and cultured Indian, a microbiologist no less, pointed at the brown river. Like the Ganges into which it flows, this is a sacred stream. 'Its water is so holy, you can fill a glass container with it, seal it, and no microbes will ever grow in the water. I know you don't believe it' – I was trying to combine scepticism with courtesy – 'but it is true' [3].

At about this time a lady approaching her 93rd birthday died in Oxford. She had been born in Moscow and was as familiar with the rites of the Russian Orthodox Church as she was with the Anglican (which was not much): she practically never attended a religious service in her life. She did, however, spend at least an hour or more praying at the foot of her bed, later on within it. Her perseverance was bolstered by the disease that had dominated the latter half of her life: obsessive compulsive disorder (OCD). Like Howard Hughes, a man as much removed from her world of philosophy and literature [4] as it is possible to be, she mumbled the same mantra of gibberish over and over. The clasping and unclasping of hands was the link between her OCD [5] and prayer [6]. During her funeral at Oxford crematorium [7], the vicar of the church in north Oxford that she never attended, said a few words. He had visited her several times towards the end of her life (she was as generous in her contributions to the parish as she was to causes that embraced both the dispossessed of sub-Saharan Africa and the Jews of Europe), and he had apparently given her Holy Communion a few days before her death. 'She was the only person I have come across who kissed my hand after I had given her the sacrament', he told the congregation. They were not particularly surprised: it had probably been the first time she had ever received the Communion, and was therefore unfamiliar with the ritual. This story probably reminds readers of the scene in Evelyn Waugh's *Brideshead Revisited*, in which the local priest administers mass to the dying unbeliever, Lord Marchmain. To me the occasion has another resonance: the lady in question was my mother.

Confused atheists

I mention these two incidents for an obvious reason. Here are two people, each of considerable intellect, in whose brains are played out emotions that are totally at odds with their otherwise rational thoughts. The same applies to millions of people, including many religious leaders, throughout the world. Virtually every bishop in the Anglican community accepts simultaneously the principle of natural selection and the benefit of prayer: the views of Richard Harries, recently retired Bishop of Oxford, are typical [8]. The late Pope, John Paul II, who was as firm a believer in God as it is possible to be, accepted Darwinian theory, and so does his successor Pope Benedict XVI. Karen Armstrong, a former nun, tries hard to redefine theism so as to make it compatible with science [9]. As Ralph Waldo Emerson said 'The religion that is afraid of science dishonors God and commits suicide.' Another cleric, the former Archbishop of York John Habgood, who has a PhD in physiology, is not disturbed by the apparent dichotomy between belief and common sense either. We corresponded a year or so ago, as I was anxious to have his views on my book *Quest: The Essence of Humanity*. 'I like your hypothesis', he wrote, 'but consider the chapter on religion its weakest part.' Unsurprised and unoffended, I replied that I hoped he did not consider my reductionist stance as offensive as that of my acquaintance Richard Dawkins, whose programme entitled *Root of All Evil?* I had watched the previous night. 'I did not switch it on', he responded, 'you see, I have a weak heart' [10].

Religious belief does not easily lend itself to scientific dissection of the underlying cause any more than does inspiration or creativity. Yet Dawkins, a distinguished zoologist who has become an internationally acclaimed author through his popularisation of science, not only attempts this, but concludes that religious belief is without foundation and is therefore to be dismissed as delusional. His attempt at analysis I admire, his conclusion I find arrogant. He sees a world without religion as one of 'no suicide bombers, no 9/11, no 7/7, no Crusades, no witch-hunts, no Gunpowder Plot, no Indian partition, no Israeli/Palestinian wars, no Serb/Croat/Muslim massacres, no persecution of Jews as "Christ-killers", no Northern Ireland "troubles", no "honour killings", no shiny-suited bouffant-haired televangelists fleecing gullible people of their money' [11]. Dawkins might do better to open his eyes to Hinduism [12]. He and other proselytising cognoscenti [13] may find few top-ranking scientists admitting to religious belief [14], but they ignore more than three billion people across the five continents – doctors and lawyers, nurses and teachers, airline pilots and bank managers, artists and artisans, widows and widowers, young and old – who derive comfort and solace from the practice of their respective religions. They give no thought to the ecclesiastical establishments in Fez and Cairo [15], in Bologna and Paris, Oxford and Cambridge, that for centuries were the only sources of education for the poor. They discount the mediaeval hospitals of Christian Europe and Muslim Arabia [16], as well as those of the New World [17] that were the only means of succour for the sick. They disregard Thomas Coram's Foundling Hospital in London, Albert Schweitzer's leper hospital in Lambarene [18] and Mother Theresa's Missions of Charity in the slums of Calcutta. They brush aside, like so much confetti, the centuries that today's faiths have endured: five millennia of Hinduism, more than three of Judaism, almost two and a half of Buddhism, 2000 years of Christianity and 1400 of Islam.

Their focus on the evils of organised religion is as blinkered as the condemnation of beneficial biotechnology by self-anointed guardians of our countryside. And what about organised atheism? Hitler's SS killed between 11 and

14 million people, Stalin's victims numbered more than 20 million, and Mao's 'Great Leap Forward' and 'Cultural' Revolution forced more than 30 million [19] innocents to their death (aside from the 62 million who died in World War II, largely at Hitler's and Stalin's hands in Russia). In Cambodia, Pol Pot brought some 1.7 million people to an early end between 1975 and 1979, while in Rwanda in 1994, between 800,000 and a million Hutus and Tutsis slaughtered each other indiscriminately. None of these massacres had anything to do with organised religion. And who tried – if only in a small way – to help some of the unfortunates, caught up in such genocides? The Christian church, for one. Cardinal Pacelli, later Pope Pius XII, may have admired Hitler and expressed no criticism of his murderous enterprise (though recent evidence suggests that, on the contrary, he subtly helped hundreds of thousands of Jews to leave Germany after 'Kristallnacht' in 1938), but simple priests and nuns saved countless lives - as did many non-believers, out of sheer human decency coupled with enormous bravery. In Poland during World War II, for example, children were hidden in religious establishments under the very noses of German troops in the same building. Those caught in the act faced arrest and execution: some 900 nuns and monks lost their lives in this way [20]. The present Rabbi of the Liberal Jewish Community in The Hague, Awraham Soetendorp, owes his life to a Catholic German couple [21].

I can vouch for one particular case. As Editor-in-Chief of an international scientific journal for over 25 years, it has been my privilege to meet the members of our editorial board from time to time. Travelling back to Europe from a scientific congress in Delhi, one scientist told me his story. His family, of Jewish origins, had managed to escape from Poland before the German invasion. In France they felt safe. When the Wehrmacht entered Paris in 1940, the Nazi commander asked the French authorities to identify all Jewish men, for transportation to Germany. The French *volunteered* [22] to add children to the lists. My friend, then a young teenager, was saved only because a Mother Superior – in spite of the potential danger to herself and her flock – took him into the school attached to her convent, hid him throughout the following four years, and educated him into the bargain (she did her job well; in adult life he became a member of the elite Académie des sciences).

Another example. During the years of Communist domination of Poland after the war, many communities suffered severely for lack of medicines. Insulin for diabetics was in particularly short supply. A committee was set up in the UK, to meet this need. As its chairman explained at a fund-raising concert in London, the only way the drugs ever reached the intended beneficiaries, was because the medicaments were delivered to a local priest. He then distributed them at the end of Sunday Mass. Anyone in need of medicines was eligible, irrespective of whether he had attended Mass or not. I could give countless examples of similar situations – in Africa and

Asia and Latin America as well as in Europe – where religious organisations have helped poor and desperate people, without a thought as to whether they were members of the faith or not. Christian Aid is one: 'We work where the need is greatest in nearly 50 countries, regardless of ethnicity, nationality or religion, to meet suffering and stop poverty – whether through providing emergency relief or long-term development' [23]. Islamic Relief is another: 'We respond to natural and man-made disasters around the world and promote sustainable economic and social development regardless of race, religion or gender' [24].

It is therefore surprising that within 283 pages packed with invective against organised religion, Christopher Hitchens [13] could not bring himself to provide a single example of altruistic behaviour on the part of a religious organisation, while Sam Harris opines that '"Respect" for other faiths, or for the views of unbelievers, is not an attitude that God endorses. ... Intolerance is ... intrinsic to every creed' [25], despite the fact that one particular *bona fide* [26] student of religion clearly states that 'Islam has had a long commitment to religious pluralism. Muhammad (recognised) Jews and Christians as protected peoples ... and there are few scriptures in the great religions of the world that can match the reverence with which the Qur'an speaks of other religious traditions' [27]. Religious debates should be conducted 'in the most kindly manner', according to the Qur'an [28]. So far as censure of religious practice and thought by today's fervent atheists is concerned, their assault is almost Epicurean [27a]. They are men behind the times. Criticism may have been pertinent in the seventeenth and eighteenth centuries. In 1770, the German-born philosopher Paul-Henri Thiry, Baron d'Holbach expressed anti-theistic arguments – 'If ignorance of nature gave birth to the Gods, knowledge of nature is destined to destroy them' [29] – that Dawkins, Harris and Hitchens merely regurgitate. As my comments about church leaders show, today's criticism is as irrelevant as chastising the Vatican for the Inquisition (for which, incidentally, it has apologised). Failure to recycle plastic bags, not apostasy, is now a sin [30]; and we haven't had a crusade since 1272.

Creationism, evolution and intelligent design
Creationism implies that a deity, be it the Hindu Brahma or the God of the Judaeo-Christian-Muslim tradition, is responsible for the fashioning of all living things. The word is used today in relation to those who reject the evidence of evolution. Those who deny man's descent, through the animal world, from a single-celled microbe. Who rebuff the analysis of rocks that shows the most ancient to be four billion years old. A creationist follows Bishop Ussher's contention, that the world was created by (his) God in 4004 BC. The rest of us, for whom science trumps myth, may be described as evolutionists [31]. Among our number are not just

agnostics and atheists, but as I have pointed out, religious leaders themselves. Incidentally, the assumption that an evolutionist necessarily does not and should not believe in a deity is misplaced. No one, scientist or philosopher, has yet provided a rational explanation for the beginning of the world: for the creation of matter (or more precisely, for the laws of physics [32]) – except Stephen Hawking [33].

By the middle of the eighteenth century, Jean-Jacques Rousseau was already speculating on the similarity between man and chimpanzee, to the extent that he classified them as a single species [34]. His contemporary Carl Linnaeus recognized the similarity, but kept them and their relatives as distinct genera: *Homo* as opposed to *Pan*. During the following century that knowledge was being assembled, and more importantly, correctly interpreted by Charles Darwin and Alfred Wallace. The evidence that living creatures – microbes, plants and animals – have evolved through the process of natural selection is clear. Creationism is as untenable as the notion that Venus is a star. Perhaps I need briefly to remind readers of the evolutionary process.

Since human beings are uppermost in the minds of creationists, let me take the emergence of humans as an example. Some six million years ago [35] there clambered through the forests of Africa an ape. Because no fossils of this particular creature have so far been found, it has no name. 'Common ancestor of today's chimpanzees and humans' is rather cumbersome. Let me simply call it 'Catch'. We know that Catch existed merely by inference. Before a creationist is moved to utter 'quite!', let me reassure readers that the inference is not open to doubt. The reason is as follows. If one analyses a human protein – say haemoglobin, the carrier of oxygen through arteries and veins – and compares it with the analogous protein from a chimpanzee, or mouse, or pigeon, or shark, one finds that the structure (the sequence in which the constituent amino acids are joined together) differs only slightly between human and chimpanzee; the difference is greater between human and mouse, even more between human and pigeon, and even more between human and shark. The same is true of any of the tens of thousands of other proteins, all of which have the same function in human, chimpanzee, mouse, pigeon and shark. We and the other animals are obviously related by virtue of our similar biochemistry, but the relationship gets weaker as one progresses backwards from human to chimpanzee to mouse to pigeon to shark. It's like comparing someone to their sibling, cousin, second cousin, or third cousin. The similarity declines.

Because the sequence of amino acids in a protein is specified by a stretch of DNA (called a gene), the same kind of relationship should be found by analysing the DNA of human, chimpanzee, mouse, pigeon and shark. The technique for analysing DNA, in other words for determining the sequence in which the constituent letters (the nucleotides A, G, C and T) are arranged, is easier to carry out than that for analysing a protein. The interpretation, however, is more difficult. This is because genes account for only around 1.5% of primate DNA [36]. The precise function of the remaining 98.5% is not at present clear. Nevertheless, the DNA of humans differs progressively from that of chimpanzees, mice, pigeons and whales, just as does the structure of their proteins. Actually the differences are much greater. Why should this be so? The answer to this question, and to the wider one of how the changes came about, are what gives credence to my inference that chimpanzees and humans are closely related through a common ancestor, Catch, that lived some six million years ago.

From around the 1950s, scientists have discovered the reason for the changes that appear in DNA. They are caused by a number of factors, chief of which are the radiations in the atmosphere that emanate from the sun. These include ultraviolet light and low levels of radioactive rays. As they impinge on living matter, they alter the letters of the DNA, by breaking the bonds that hold them together and allowing other letters to take their place. I do not mean that some of the letters (A, G, C and T) are replaced by quite different ones. The effect of the radiations is to replace, say an A by a G, C, or T, a G by an A, C or T, and so on. Sometimes an extra letter is added, sometimes one is removed. These reactions are known as mutations [37], and they occur, willy-nilly, anywhere along the DNA sequence. One stretch of DNA is like another, so mutations are totally random. They occur as much in the 1.5% gene, or protein-coding, regions, as in the remaining 98.5% non-coding region. Mutations within the 98.5% have relatively little effect on the survival of the creature in which they occur. But mutations within the 1.5% gene regions, by affecting the structure and hence the efficiency of proteins for which they code, do. Generally the effect is deleterious, and creatures carrying mutations within these regions of their DNA do not survive. Hence those that do survive from one generation to the next, show less variability in the 1.5% gene regions than in the rest of their DNA.

In addition to 'neutral' mutations in a protein-coding region (neither deleterious nor beneficial), very occasionally a mutation in such a region will improve the efficacy of the protein concerned. Such mutations will not die out, but be retained. A slightly-altered protein in an animal living in a particular environmental niche may give it an advantage over its fellows. This is the basis of natural selection, and I will give an example shortly. Before losing the thread of this narrative, I need to justify my assertion that Catch lived around six million years ago. The amount of radiation falling on the earth has been fairly constant over that time, and so, therefore, has the rate of mutation in DNA. It is about one change per 100 million letters per generation [38]. In a human or a chimpanzee, with 3 billion letters in its DNA, this means 60 changes (0.000001%) every 20 years or so [39]. By assessing the number of changes that have occurred, one has a kind of 'molecular clock' that ticks backwards in time. Based on the approximate generation times of humans, chimpanzees, mice, pigeons and sharks, we can use this molecular clock to tell us when two species diverged. The number of letters that are different in a human compared with a chimpanzee points to their common ancestor, Catch, having lived around six million years ago. From that time onwards, mutations that proved favourable occurred in the lineage leading to humans in several regards: the ability to walk upright, that allows earlier vision of predator or prey across the savannah and that frees the hands for other tasks; a greater flexibility of thumb, that makes the fashioning of tools possible; a more elaborate vocal cord, that allows sophisticated communication through speech; and three times as many nerve cells in the brain, that enables more complicated reasoning to take place [40].

But why did Catch's progeny diverge at all? Why didn't they continue to mate and share their genes as a single species? Because something happened to gradually isolate two groups of Catch, as a result of which their descendants evolved into separate species. This prevented their mating, or rather it prevented the birth of viable offspring: two separate but closely related species, like horse and donkey, can mate, but the result is a sterile mule. We do not know what that something was, that separated the two groups, and can only speculate. Perhaps one troupe of Catch continued to live among the branches of trees in the forest and evolved into today's chimpanzees, whereas the other started to inhabit the neighbouring savannah and evolved into today's humans. In other cases we do know what causes a species to bifurcate. It was Charles Darwin's insight into the origin of the differences between the predominant species of finch, that he observed on the various islands of the Galapagos, that was one of the factors that enabled him to formulate the origin of species.

Darwin noted that the beaks of finches found on an island containing mainly edible nuts were different from those of finches found on an island containing mainly edible fruit. The beaks of the former were adapted to eating nuts, the beaks of the latter to eating fruit. The reason the finches from the various islands did not mate, and hence cause a smoothing out of any differences in beak shape, was that the islands had become further and further separated (through tectonic shift) from each other over time: the island-hopping ability of the finches could no longer cope with the distances involved. Originally, Darwin assumed, there had been just one large island, and one species of finch. The movement of land masses away from each other, like Madagascar from the rest of Africa [41], and rising sea levels or flooding, like that responsible for the formation of the English Channel [42], are what create evolutionary niches, and they confirm Darwin's hunch.

I referred in the opening chapter to the necessity of teachers and politicians to have a proper grasp of science, in order that they may transmit this to our youngsters. In many areas of the world this is no longer the case. The erudition of the Abbasid caliphs of Baghdad in the ninth century, and of their Umaiyid rivals of Cordoba in the tenth, has been replaced by ignorance and wanton disregard of the Qur'an by the Taliban in Afghanistan during the twentieth. These intemperate suppressors of enlightenment seem to have forgotten that 'seek knowledge' is one of the Prophet Muhammad's own commands. Retrograde education resurfaced in England a decade ago, when a school in Gateshead decided to teach creationism alongside evolution. The idea was that the students should be encouraged to compare the two concepts, as though they were alternatives. They are not. One is a myth, the other fact. They are as disparate as dreaming and cleaning one's teeth, or as the writing of poetry and riding a bicycle. Yet creationism is gaining ground in Britain: in a recent survey, over half of those polled said they would like to see creationism taught alongside evolution, and only a quarter believe that evolution alone should be taught in science lessons in schools – a proportion that, surprisingly, is lower than in countries like Spain, with its strongly Roman Catholic tradition, or India, many of whose population are devout Hindus or Muslims [43].

In several southern states of the USA, evolution isn't even an option. Such fundamentalism is a recent phenomenon. In 1922, the most religious president ever to have occupied the White House, was asked for his view of Darwin's theory. 'Of course I do believe in organic evolution', Woodrow Wilson replied. 'It surprises me that at this late date such questions should be raised' [44]. Yet Wilson was also an avowed Christian, who prayed daily: 'I do not see how anyone can sustain himself in any enterprise in life without prayer' [45].

I mention the first of Woodrow Wilson's remarks because it was made just three years before the most famous confrontation between creationists and evolutionists took place. The battle was played out not in a chamber of Congress, not in the debating hall of a great university, not in the salons of Washington, but in the sleepy courtroom of the small town of Dayton, Tennessee. The state had passed a law forbidding the teaching of evolution: '... it shall be unlawful for any teacher in any of the Universities, Normals and all other public schools of the State ... to teach any theory that denies the story of the Divine Creation of man as taught in the Bible, and to teach instead that man has descended from a lower order of animals.' The American Civil Liberties Union (ACLU) decided to contest the law and found a willing party to challenge the edict, by openly teaching the basics of evolution according to Darwin's *Origin of Species*. That person was actually the football coach of Rhea County High School, but he was prepared to incite the authorities by admitting this heinous act of education, for which he was duly indicted. His name was John T Scopes.

The Scopes monkey trial, as it came to be called, lasted over a week. It was, in a sense, America's version of the T H Huxley – Bishop Wilberforce debate that took place at Oxford in 1860. The defence team was strenghened by the presence of the famous Clarence Darrow: the case proved to be one of the few he ever lost. The proceedings were a farce from beginning to end. The witness of eminent scientists to the proven facts of evolution (the writer H G Wells rightly turned down an invitation to testify) was not allowed. Darrow's cross-examination of the chief prosecutor, William Jennings Bryan, regarding his religious beliefs ('yes the earth was 5929 years old [46]; yes Eve was created from Adam's rib', and so on), was struck from the record. The only sensible comments that emanated from the trial were those of H L Mencken, who covered the proceedings for the *Baltimore Sun*: 'The inferior man's reasons for hating knowledge are not hard to discern. He hates it because it is complex – because it puts an unbearable burden upon his meagre capacity for taking in ideas. Thus his search is always for short cuts. All superstitions are such short cuts. Their aim is to make the unintelligible simple, and even obvious. ... the cosmogony of Genesis is so simple even a yokel can grasp it' [47]. The ways by which new species emerge – be it animal, plant or microbe – are, by contrast, quite complicated. Mencken, who was an intellectual snob as well as a social one, may have referred to the 'inferior man's ... meagre capacity for taking in ideas', but some very superior men (heads of nations not excluded) fit the bill equally well. Indeed, it is this attitude among politicians and bureaucrats that is responsible for the educational dumbing-down that we are witnessing on both sides of the Atlantic today.

I said right at the start of this book that people are entitled to hold views that are at odds with accepted wisdom, but the fact that 47% of Americans consider God to 'have created human beings pretty much in their present form at one time within the last 10,000 years or so', with a mere 11% accepting the secular account of evolution, and 68% supportive of the view that creationism should be taught in biology classes [48], is worrying. For it means that more than a 100 million people are creationists of one sort or another. While this includes virtually no scientist of stature, it surely comprises thousands of schoolteachers, administrators, lawmakers, politicians, journalists and film producers. Indeed, when ten Republican candidates for the presidency were asked during a televised debate in May of 2007 whether they believed in evolution, three answered 'no'. Such views may win the votes of Hill-Billies from Arkansas, but they are unlikely to prevent the downward slide of the USA as a world-class power *vis-à-vis* its competitors from China, India and Japan.

In 1987, more than 60 years after the Scopes Monkey Trial, the trend was reversed. In that year the Supreme Court of the United States ruled against the teaching of creationism alongside evolution on the grounds that this violates the clause prohibiting state aid to religion. Creationists were finally under threat. Their leaders sat down, needless to say with lawyers at their side – the very founder (Phillip Johnson) of the movement they initiated, is a lawyer – and, following the eighteenth century cleric William Paley, as well as the views of Plato, came up with the notion of 'intelligent design' (ID). This idea obviates the need to postulate the hand of God in creating the universe as we know it. Just who or what is represented as the intelligent designer was left deliberately vague. The idea took hold and at the end of lectures to lay audiences on 'What makes us human?' I am no longer asked whether I believe in divine creation, but whether I believe in intelligent design. The basis of the movement is that certain features of living organisms, such as the wing of a dragonfly, the eye of an eagle, the flagellar motor of a bacterium (that enables it to move towards a source of nutrients), the cascade of reactions leading to the clotting of blood or to the generation of immunity against disease, are just too complicated to be achieved by the evolutionary mechanism of natural selection alone.

Picking apparently complex systems as opposed to simpler ones reveals an ignorance of biochemistry (even though one of the supporters of ID is himself a biologist): that all life depends on the interactive function of proteins, and that the precise nature of these processes within a dragonfly, eagle, bacterium or human is specified by the genes (stretches of DNA) responsible for the synthesis and activity of proteins. The seeming absence of plausible mechanisms to explain the evolutionary origin of the genes concerned in the above examples proferred by the proponents of intelligent design has been well refuted by a number of authors [49]. Darwin knew none of these underlying mechanisms when he postulated the origin of species, which is why his theory was such a prophetic *tour de force*. Only a century after his time have scientists been able to explain every nuance of natural selection in terms of molecular interactions. Which is why scientists – and every schoolchild trained in science – accept evolution as unreservedly as they do the principle of Archimedes or that of gravity. But H L Mencken was right: grasping the details of biochemistry and physiology, of genetics and immunology, requires greater mental effort than reciting the first few verses of Genesis.

Religious belief

'That God does not exist, I cannot deny. That my whole being cries out for God, I cannot forget', confessed Jean-Paul Sartre. Somewhat paradoxically he also said 'I do not feel that I am the product of chance, a speck of dust in the universe, but someone who was expected, prepared, prefigured. In short, a being whom only a Creator could put here; and this idea of a creating hand refers to God' [50]. Sartre considered himself a humanist, but whether the anti-religious coterie of today would admit him into their club in the light of the latter remark, I doubt. The point is that he was a twentieth century *savant*, unable to reject religion out of hand. What is the basis of its unremitting appeal? Richard Dawkins considers that the survival of religion may be a by-product of something quite different: the obedience of children to their parents [51]. At the dawn of civilisation, when the actions of invisible deities were the best explanations for the rising of the sun and the phases of the moon, for the ripening of harvest and the birth of a child, when it was reasonable to invoke a God to bring on rain in order to ward off famine, it was also imperative to tell children not to swim in crocodile-infested waters and not to pick up red hot embers from a fire. Such strictures have obvious survival value, and listening to your parents' advice was passed from generation to generation. At the same time, of course, children learnt to follow their parents' lead in prayer and supplication. Why adults should continue to pass religious notions to their children after they stopped believing themselves, is not made clear. This by-product hypothesis is attractive, though, as a generalised explanation for the passing on of cultural modes, that Dawkins calls 'memes' [52]. Religion is one of the most pervasive of memes. Other writers have provided by-product scenarios in terms that are different from that of childhood obedience. Robin Dunbar considers religious practice to underlie the very evolution of modern man [53] and Jesse Bering follows a similar line [54]. None of this, of course, explains Sartre's 'my whole being cries out for God'. Does religious belief have any intrinsic value?

A decade ago I suggested that it might, and that this is part of the placebo effect [55]. Let me remind readers of the placebo effect [56]. It refers to the situation in which a person *thinks* he has been given a proven medicine for some ailment, when in fact all he has received is a similar-looking, and similar-tasting, but quite ineffective, product. The placebo effect has been defined as 'the effect of any therapeutic procedure or substance that lacks the *specific* power to help a condition being treated' [57]. Clinical researchers use it to measure a new drug's efficacy. Patients suffering from a malady, be it rheumatism or heart disease or terminal cancer, are divided into two, approximately equal, groups. One group receives the medicament under trial (often not yet fully proven to be efficacious, but shown to be non-toxic), the other gets the placebo. Neither the patient nor the clinician who is assessing the efficacy of the drug knows which group is which (the drug and its substitute have simply been labelled A and B by a laboratory technician, who keeps the record). In many trials of this sort, known for obvious reasons as 'double blind', the placebo effect is remarkably high – some 30% of patients improve; if the number who improve with the placebo is the same as those who improve with the drug, then the drug itself is considered to be without effect. One explanation for this is that the drug is only weakly active anyway, and those who got better did so spontaneously. Another explanation is that the patient's positive thinking that he is being cured, is the cause. In other words the placebo effect is not all 'neutral': part is due to an actual molecular change within the patient's body. The supposition that mind and body are two separate entities is no longer valid. In fact Descartes' 'I think therefore I am' is nearer the mark than people realised at the time (this is not, of course, what he had in mind when he coined the phrase). Several substances that modify nerve transmission in the brain also have an effect on the gut. There is continuous cross-talk between the brain and the rest of the body. The sudden bowel movement that occurs when one is under stress of one sort or another is a potent example.

There is much evidence that positive thinking can ameliorate certain diseases by reducing the stress that they cause. Meditation, religious belief and prayer fall into this category. The benefits are as real as those of an actual sleeping pill or a pain killer, because the underlying neural mechanisms are similar. Perhaps we should rename the effect *placet* (it pleases me) rather than placebo. In an earlier work [58] I drew attention to the fact that religiosity owes much to our fear of death, and that this is largely a consequence of man's consciousness of himself. Fear leads to stress; religious belief counters it. In his television presentation *Root of All Evil?* Richard Dawkins noted disparagingly that the recovery rate of patients visiting Lourdes for a miracle cure is no higher than the placebo effect. Precisely so, because religious belief contributes to the effect for some people, just as music or art or the beauty of the countryside does for others. Dawkins actually acknowledges this point, though somewhat as an aside [59], while Harris mentions it but then rapidly rejects the notion [60].

Most believers, I fancy, would agree that their God exists largely in their mind. Buddhists may venerate their founder Siddhartha Gautama, but they do not subscribe to the notion that the creatures on this earth were brought to life by the hand of a god. The very word 'buddha' means 'enlightenment' in Sanskrit. Buddhists believe in the beneficial effects of prayer, which is why their sect has become so popular with Westerners in recent times [61]. The followers of the Dalai Lama, who have left Tibet in order to live in Dharmsala, a settlement set high in the foothills of the Himalayas in northern India, provide a good example of the power of the mind over the body.

Dr Herbert Benson, an American physician from Harvard Medical School, has studied the effects of emotional stress on body parameters such as blood pressure. As stress increases, so does blood pressure. This can lead to atherosclerosis, heart attacks and strokes. Reversing stress – the so-called 'relaxation response' – reduces blood pressure and its attendant consequences. In the mid-1980s, Benson and a small team of scientists went to Dharmsala to see whether they could detect any physical outcome of meditation. They decided to measure the monks' temperature at various body extremeties before, during, and after periods of intense meditation. In the case of senior monks, they found an increased temperature after meditation for various periods. Some of the novices did not show this. The monks themselves had recognised this. 'These Tibetan Buddhists ... are well aware that the amount of heat they produce is significant. In fact, they evaluate how far along a neophyte is in his practice of the Yoga by the amount of heat he can produce. For example, they may all be asked to sit together outside on the moist, early-morning ground. The more proficient meditators can keep their skin dry with the heat they emanate, while the skin of the less able monks becomes moist from the morning dew' [62].

A raised temperature of the skin indicates that its blood vessels have become dilated. This means that blood pressure falls, which is one of the aims of the relaxation response. Yoga-type meditation is not the only way to attain this. Religious belief of any flavour helps to elicit the ingredients of the 'relaxation response'. This encompasses a lowering of heart rate (pulse) and breathing, a slowing of brain waves and general metabolism, as well as a decrease of blood pressure. The reader will appreciate that belief plays only a minor part in this sequence of steps that Dr Benson claims will, among other things, 'break the anxiety cycle and relieve the anxiety-related symptoms of nausea, vomiting, diarrhoea, constipation, and short-temperedness; combat attacks of hyperventilation; alleviate the pains of headache, backache and other pains, such as angina pectoris; effectively treat many types of hypertension and heartbeat irregularities; alleviate insomnia; prevent the harmful effects of stress' [63]. These are pretty obvious sequels to a typical meditation routine. I mention Dr Benson's 'relaxation response' [64] only to indicate that religious belief can contribute towards a beneficial outcome of meditation.

Other reports indicate that religiosity is good for you. Religious belief may help you to overcome pain [65], and in certain situations religious people enjoy longer lives than non-religious folk. Apart from anecdotal evidence in this regard, a detailed analysis of the life expectancy of religious versus secular communes in nineteenth century America came to the conclusion that members of the former were four times as likely to live to a longer age than members of the latter [66].

The thoughts that ping through our brain are sometimes rational, sometimes not. As a young child my fear of snakes (I had seen these only in a circus) was so great, I could not bear to even touch a picture depicting these reptiles. I am told that this dislike may be hard-wired in my brain, since such fear would have been advantageous to our primate ancestors [67]. I am more ape than I thought. The point I wish to make is that illogical thoughts are part of our mental make up. 'Our brains are belief engines ... Superstition and belief in magic are millions of years old' [68]. In my case, snakes are real, but their pictures aren't. In prayer, the converse holds. The object of one's prayer may not be real, but belief in the efficacy of invocation is.

Life for most of us is hard and cruel. It was so in the Stone Age, and it is still so today. Not, nowadays, because of the uncertainty of finding a tree laden with edible fruit, or a gazelle within range of a spear, but because of the stresses that civilisation has brought: worry about our job, anxiety about money, concern about our children's education. Even before the Stone Age, listening to stories at the end of a day's hunting was a relaxing experience. According to Robin Dunbar, it marked the very beginning of language [69].

My point is simple. Our brains, that started to become dramatically more complex around six million years ago, have become attuned to responding with satisfaction to an amalgamation of fact and fiction. We know where in the brain feelings of pleasure are registered: in a primitive area that developed over a hundred million years ago, and that we now share with the lowly crocodile. The area comprises the inner region of the limbic system known as the caudate nucleus. There are those who ascribe to particular parts within the caudate nucleus, receptors that are sensitive to specific stimuli. Helen Fisher believes she has identified the receptors that respond to falling in love [70]. Her conclusion is based on the technique of functional magnetic resonance imaging (fMRI). This is a non-invasive method of tracking the pathways in the brain that are activated when someone performs a particular action. The person is placed inside a nuclear magnetic resonance machine, and the increased blood flow that accompanies activation of the affected neurons (nerve cells) is revealed by contrast imaging. Specific areas 'light up' as a result of just crooking a finger, or working out sums. Or falling in love. In this case it is dopaminergic pathways [71] in the caudate nucleus that light up. These areas constitute millions of neurons, so the method is not fine enough to distinguish individual cells and fibres. As I have pointed out elsewhere [72], what the fMRI images show is probably the wider feeling of pleasure: put me inside an MRI machine and show me a caviar blini, or play me the music of Schubert, and my brain might light up in the same regions as those of the SUNY graduate students when shown pictures of their loved one. My guess is that undergoing religious experiences, or just praying, might reveal the same 'gratification' areas. Richard Dawkins (in another television documentary) once had himself tested by fMRI in order to see whether a 'God centre' is present in the human brain, but of course the experiment failed. Not because Dawkins is a non-believer, but because the concept of a deity is too recent, in evolutionary terms, for such a specific structure to have evolved.

People in desperate situations, like facing death on the edge of a mountain precipice or on an upturned boat in a turbulent ocean or lost in the desert without food and water, often turn to prayer. According to the writer Wilfrid Noyce, those who survive are not necessarily physically the strongest. 'What seems to count most is an inner psychological strength, which is nurtured by purpose, hope and spiritual beliefs. ... Survivors of long ordeals regularly report that their will to live was sustained by the thought of a specific goal or task they needed to achieve – with such unfinished business, they could not allow themselves to die ...' Prayer, Noyce found, can provide people with a remarkable resilience. This was true even for people who were not religious prior to their ordeal. ... 'Those who are able to reach a "spiritual second wind", may endure in ways that defy imagination' [73]. Another example comes from the inmates of Auschwitz. 'One day a group of Jews decided to put God on trial. In the face of such inconceivable suffering, they found the conventional arguments utterly unconvincing. ... They condemned God to death. The presiding rabbi pronounced the verdict, then went on calmly that it was time for the evening prayer. Ideas about God come and go, but prayer, the struggle to find meaning even in the darkest circumstances, must continue' [74]. Mind and soul used to be thought of as black boxes, somehow separate from the rest of the body. Most of us no longer accept this notion: the boxes are still black, but we are beginning to discern their texture. They are part of the neural network that constitutes a large part of our brain. The time has come to recognise that certain types of belief – whether in the healing effect of a substitute pill or in the calming effect of prayer to an imagined deity – produce physiological changes [75]. The stimuli are as real as those that lead to an increased appetite for food or sex.

Richard Dawkins is upset that atheism is not better supported in the USA; other minority groups, like homosexuals, receive more lavish funding. I am concerned that fanatics in the Middle East encourage youngsters to terrorize with impunity the citizens of any country, Islamic or not, that they decide to target. Dawkins and fellow atheists consider religious faith to be largely evil. I believe it to be predominantly benign. They think religion should be suppressed. I think it should be respected. The anger of Muslim fundamentalists has less to do with religion than with envy of the West and its better scientific know-how, and with disillusion of their leaders' performance over the past eighty years [76].

The knowledge we have of nature – of the evolution of plants and animals, of the origin of galaxies, stars and planets – should be taught to every child, from Kansas to Kamchatka, from Cairo to Cape Horn. The validity of science is universal: it lends itself to forging international bonds even more than does art or literature or sport. To achieve these aims we must strive to eliminate scientific ignorance. But we should do so without arrogance. Let us not forget that in the Masai language the words for 'God' and 'I do not know' are the same [77].

The main import of this chapter is simple: creationism is myth, evolution is fact, intelligent design is neither. Youngsters should be taught creationism during religious study, not in science lessons: the Bible is a book of parables, not a compendium of contemporary knowledge. My other point is equally obvious: to disregard the benefits of religious practice and belief is both arrogant and obtuse.

I find myself somewhat in sympathy with writer Alain de Botton [78], and especially with physicist Freeman Dyson. 'As human beings, we are groping for knowledge and understanding of the strange universe into which we are born. We have many ways of understanding, of which science is only one. Our thought processes are only partially based on logic, and are inextricably mixed with emotions and desires and social interactions. We cannot live as isolated intelligences, but only as members of a working community. Our ways of understanding have been collective, beginning with the stories that we told one another around the fire when we lived in caves. Our ways today are still collective, including literature, history, art, music, religion, and science. Science is a particular bunch of tools that have been conspicuously successful for understanding and manipulating the material universe. Religion is another bunch of tools, giving us hints of a mental or spiritual universe that transcends the material universe' [79].

Notes

[1]   Benjamin Disraeli: *Sybil. Or the Two Nations.* (first published 1845; republished in the Penguin English Library, 1980)

[2]   The feathered serpent deity of the Maya, taken over by the Aztecs as Quetzalcoatl

[3]   I recounted this event in an earlier book, *Quest: The Essence of Humanity* (Wiley, Chichester, 2003), and admit it to avoid accusations of self-plagiarism

[4]   Frequent visitors at her house were the ebullient Warden of Wadham (Maurice Bowra) and the equally loquacious Chichele Professor of Social and Political Theory (Isiah Berlin), who would vie with each other for verbal supremacy

[5]   Roughly 2% of people suffer from OCD. Genetically-modified mice have recently been shown to display symptoms similar to OCD (Steven E Hyman: Obsessed with grooming. *Nature* 448: 871-2, 2007 and Jeffrey M Welch *et al*: Cortico-striatal synaptic defects and OCD-like behaviours in *Sapap3*-mutant mice. *Nature* 448: 894-900, 2007). This should aid in developing new drugs to combat the disease

[6]   Religious rituals and OCD may actually share a neurophysiological cause: see (the appropriately first-named) Pascal Boyer: Religion: Bound to believe? *Nature* 455: 1038-9, 2008

[7]   The place of her husband's cremation 17 years earlier; she kept his remains in a jar in her larder, easily confused for a container of sugar by the carers who looked after in her latter years

[8]   Richard Harries: *'Half Ape, Half Angel'?* in Charles Pasternak, ed: *What Makes Us Human?* (Oneworld Publications, Oxford, 2007), pp 71-81

[9]   Karen Armstrong: *The Case for God. What Religion Really Means.* (The Bodley Head, London, 2009)

[10]   Archbishop Habgood also pointed out that Dawkins, in his youth, had been a fervent Evangelist, a fact not apparent from reading his books

[11]   Richard Dawkins: *The God Delusion* (Black Swan, London, 2007), p 25

[12]   'I am no Hindu, but I hold the doctrines for the Hindus concerning a future state to be incomparably more rational, more pious and more likely to deter men from vice than the horrid opinions inculcated by the Christians on punishment without end' Sir William Jones, Justice of the new Supreme Court at Calcutta, wrote in 1787 to the second Earl Spencer. Quoted by William Dalrymple: *White Mughals. Love & Betrayal in Eighteenth-Century India* (Flamingo, London, 2003), p 42

[13]   Sam Harris: *Letter to a Christian Nation* (Knopf, 2006) and Christopher Hitchens: *God Is Not Great* (Hachette Book Group, 2007). Less strident views, with intellectually sound argument, are expressed by Dan Dennett: *Breaking the Spell: Religion as a Natural Phenomenon* (Viking Penguin, 2006) and Jesse Bering: *The God Instinct. The Psychology of Souls, Destiny, and the Meaning of Life* (Nicholas Brealey Publishing, London 2011)

[14]   Though the Whitley Professor of Biochemistry at Oxford – a Nobel Laureate – read nightly from the Bible by his bedside. Other exceptions include Francis Collins: *The Language of God*, Owen Gingerich: *God's Universe* (Belknap, Cambridge, MA, 2006) and John Polkinghorne: *Faith, Science and Understanding* (SPCK, London, 2000)

[15]   Jami'at al-Qarawiyyin and Al-Azhar respectively, two of the oldest centres
       of learning in the world

[16]   The sixth century hospital at Mérida and the ninth century hospitals of
       Baghdad, respectively, probably being among the first. By the sixteenth
       century, the hospital of the Knights of St John at Rhodes had become 'the
       best in Christendom' [John Julius Norwich: *Venice. The Greatness and the
       Fall* (Allen Lane, London, 1981), p 184

[17]   The sixteenth century Hospital de Jesús Nazareno in Mexico City and the
       seventeenth century Hôtel de Dieu ('hostel of God') in Quebec being
       among the oldest in central and north America, respectively

[18]   In Gabon, west central Africa

[19]   Some put the number as high as 37 million: Will Hutton: *The Writing on
       the Wall. China and the West in the 21st Century* (Abacus, London, 2007),
       p 83

[20]   Michael Burleigh: *Moral Combat. A History of World War II* (Harper
       Press, London, 2010), p 470

[21]   Green Cross International (ed): *Mikhail Gorbachev: Prophet of Change.
       From the Cold War to a sustainable world* (Clairview Books, Forest Row,
       East Sussex, 2011), p 305

[22]   The person responsible was René Bousquet, a Vichy collaborator; see
       Edmund White in NY Review of Books, June 26, 2008, p 30

[23]   See http://www.christianaid.org.uk/

[24]   See http://www.islamic-relief.com/

[25]   Sam Harris: *The End of Faith. Religion, Terror, and the future of Reason*
       (The Free Press, London, 2005), p 13

[26]   Harvard, Santa Clara University, and the University of California at Santa
       Barbara

[27]   Rheas Aslan: *No god but God. The Origins, Evolution, and Future of Islam* (William Heinemann, London, 2005) p 262

[27a] Epicurus (341-270 BC) was a materialist who attacked superstition and divine intervention

[28]   Karen Armstrong, p 310 (see note 9 above)

[29]   In *Système de la Nature* (1770) pt 2, ch 1; from *Oxford Dictionary of Quotations* (1999). Holbach mixed with the greatest minds of his age: the marquis de Condorcet, Denis Diderot, Edward Gibbon, David Hume, Jean-Jacques Rousseau, Adam Smith and Horace Walpole all dined off his lavish table in Paris

[30]   *Daily Telegraph*, March 10, 2008

[31]   A good account of the difference between creationism and evolution is given in a booklet entitled *Science, Evolution and Creationism* (National Academies Press, 2008), a summary of which can be downloaded free from http://www.nap.edu

[32]   Paul Davies: *The Goldilocks Enigma. Why is the universe just right for life?* (Allen Lane, London, 2006)

[33]   Stephen Hawking and Leonard Modinow: *The Grand Design* (Bantam Press, London, 2010

[34]   See Carl Sagan and Ann Druyan: *Shadows of Forgotten Ancestors. A Search for Who We Are* (Random House, New York, 1992) p 273

[35]   The time at which chimps and humans began to diverge could be considerably less. Studies such as those of Asger Hobolth *et al*: Genomic relationships and speciation times of human, chimpanzee, and gorilla inferred from a coalescent hidden Markov model. *PloS Genetics* 3(2): e7. (doi: 10.1371/journal. pgen.0030007) estimate it to have been around four million years ago. They also show that the population size of Catch was surprisingly large: some 50,000 members. The problem about dating common ancestors is that genetic differences between two species are not the same throughout the whole genome. See Richard A Gibbs and Jeffrey

Rogers: Gorilla gorilla gorilla. *Nature* 483: 164-165 (2012) and Aylwyn
Scully et al: Insights into hominid evolution from the gorilla genome
sequence. *Nature* 483: 169-175, 2012

[36] As opposed to viruses, like the HIV mentioned in chapter 3, in which genes
account for 100% of the genome

[37] From the Latin word *muto*, meaning change

[38] Francis S Collins: *The Language of God* (Free Press, New York, 2006) p 131

[39] The figure is 60, not 30, because animals have two sets of DNA, one
inherited from each parent, within them. A recent figure of 70 new
mutations per genome of a human between successive generations, that has
been obtained by direct analysis of two siblings and their parents (*Nature*
464: 329, 2010) sits pretty well with the earlier number

[40] See Charles Pasternak: *Quest: The Essence of Humanity* (Wiley,
Chichester, 2003) pp 73-101 for details

[41] The Indian sub-continent split from Africa around 170 million years ago.
As it drifted north towards Eurasia, Madagascar became detached from *it*
some 90 million years later

[42] Flooding, perhaps caused by an earthquake, is believed to have destroyed
the isthmus joining Britain to mainland Europe between 450,000 and
180,000 years ago

[43] Ipsos MORI.survey of Oct 2009

[44] Francis Wheen: *How Mumbo-Jumbo Conquered the World. A Short
History of Modern Delusions* (Fourth Estate, London, 2004), p 109

[45] From Sigmund Freud and William C Bullitt: *Thomas Woodrow Wilson.
Twenty-eighth President of the United States. A Psychological Study.*
(Weidenfeld and Nicolson, London, 1967), p 7

[46] ie in 1925

[47]   Francis Wheen, p 111

[48]   Ibid, p 103

[49]   For example by Kenneth Miller in *Finding Darwin's God* (New York: HarperCollins, 1999), by Francis Collins, op cit, p 189, by JT Bridgham, SM Carroll and JW Thornton: Evolution of hormone-receptor complexity by molecular exploitation. *Science* 312: 97-101 (2006): summarised by Helen Pearson: Raising the dead. *Nature* 483: 390-393, 2012, and by Kevin Padian: see http://www.sciohost.org/ncse/kvd/Padian/Padian_transcript.html. The apparent difficulty of accounting for the evolution of the eye is well dismissed by Nick Lane: *A Life Ascending. The Ten Great Inventions of Evolution* (Profile Books, London, 2010), pp 172-204

[50]   Quoted in Norman L Geisler: *Is Man the Measure? An Evaluation of Contemporary Humanism* (1983) pp 46-47

[51]   Dawkins, op cit, p 200 et seq; see also Jesse Bering: *The God Instinct: The Psychology of Souls, Destiny and the Meaning of Life* (Nicholas Brealey Publishing, London, 2010)

[52]   Richard Dawkins: *The Selfish Gene* (Oxford University Press, Oxford, 1976)

[53]   Robin Dunbar: *How Many Friends Does One Person Need? Dunbar's Number and other evolutionary quirks* (Faber and Faber, London, 2010), pp 278-292

[54]   Jesse Bering: *The God Instinct. The psychology of souls, destiny, and the meaning of life.* (Nicholas Brealey Publishing, London, 2011)

[55]   Charles Pasternak: *The Molecules Within Us: Our Body in Health and Disease* (Plenum, New York, 1998), chapters 6 and 7

[56]   The word comes from the Latin *placebo* = I will please. In other words, I will please the patient by giving him something to improve his condition, even though I know it to be ineffectual

[57]   Herbert Benson with William Proctor: *Beyond the Relaxation Response. How to Harness the Healing Power of Your Personal Beliefs* (Collins, Fount Paperbacks, London, 1985), p 133

[58]   *Quest: The Essence of Humanity* pp 250, 273 (see note 40)

[59]   Richard Dawkins: *The God Delusion*, p 194

[60]   Sam Harris: *Letter to a Christian Nation*, p 47

[61]   See, for example, Donald S Lopez: *Buddhism and Science: A Guide for the Perplexed* (University of Chicago Press, 2008) and Pier Luigi, with Zara Houshmand: *Mind and Life: Discussions with the Dalai Lama on the Nature of Reality* (Columbia University Press, 2008); also Joseph Seckbach and Richard Gordon (eds): *Divine Action and Natural Selection. Science, Faith and Evolution* (World Scientific, Singapore/Imperial College Press, London, 2008

[62]   Herbert Benson with William Proctor, p 60

[63]   Ibid, pp 97-108

[64]   A vindication of Herbert Benson's findings appeared in 2007: Y-Y Tang *et al*. Short-term meditation training improves attention and self-regulation. *Proc Natl Acad Sci, USA* 104: 17,152-17,156, 2007

[65]   Katja Wiech et al: An fMRI study measuring analgesia enhanced by religion as a belief system. *Pain* 139: 467-476, 2009

[66]   Ara Norenzayan and Azim F. Shariff: *The Origin and Evolution of Religious Prosociality Science* 322: 58-62, 2008

[67]   Eliminating such fear is not as easy as it seems; see Pankaj Sah and R Frederick Westbrook: The circuit of fear. *Nature* 454: 589-590, 2008

[68]   Michael Shermer: Wheatgrass juice and folk medicine, *Scientific American* vol 299, August 2008, p 26; also by him is *The Believing Brain: From Ghosts and Gods to Politics and Conspiracies – How We Construct Beliefs and Reinforce Them as Truths* (Times Books, New York, 2011); see also John F Hoffecker: *Landscape of the Mind: Human Evolution and the Archaeology of Thought* (Columbia University Press, New York, 2011)

[69] *Grooming, Gossip and the Evolution of Language* (Faber and Faber, London, 1996)

[70] Helen Fisher: *Why We Love: The Nature and Chemistry of Romantic Love* (Henry Holt & Co, New York, 2004)

[71] Dopamine is one of the molecules that transmits nerve impulses

[72] Charles Pasternak: *The Science of Love* (www.firstscience.com/SITE/ARTICLES/love.asp , 2005)

[73] From Robert Whitaker: *The Mapmaker's Wife* (Delta Books, New York, 2005), pp 271-273

[74] From Karen Armstrong, p 266 (see note 9, above)

[75] Charles Pasternak: Placebo: no longer a phantom response. *Interdisciplinary Science Reviews* 36: 73-84, 2011

[76] I wrote these words before I read Alister McGrath's *The Dawkins Delusion? Atheist fundamentalism and the denial of the divine* (SPCK, London, 2007): he too draws attention (pp 46-49) to the naïvety of assuming a religious basis for international terror, by citing other examples. In contrast, the Indian Mutiny of 1857, thought by some to be the prelude for getting the British out of India (that was achieved ninety years later), was in fact a religious war, not a political one. One of the key triggers was to coat the bullets, that the sepoys had to 'bite' (in order to separate the powder, which was poured down the bore of the rifle, from the ball, which then followed it) with a mixture of pig and cow fat. This offended both Muslims and Hindus. See William Dalrymple: *The Last Mughal. The Fall of a Dynasty, Delhi, 1857* (Bloomsbury, London, 2006)

[77] Roderick Graham: *The Great Infidel. A Life of David Hume* (Birlinn, Edinburgh, 2006), p 75

[78] Alain de Botton: *Religion for Atheists. A non-believer's guide to the uses of religion* (Hamish Hamilton, London, 2012)

[79] Freeman Dyson: *The Scientist as Rebel* (New York Review of Books, New York, 2006), p 350

CHAPTER 6

One culture, one solution

THE bell of the Baroque *Chiesa Matrice* (Mother Church), situated high up in the old *Centro Storico* of Amantea, is tolling for matins. It is a hot Calabrian August day, but the air is cool within the study of the eighteenth century palazzo next door. Looking out of the window, other churches and ancient buildings shimmer in the haze. Below, in a small square surrounded by narrow alleys, traders are setting out their wares: fish and fowl, fruit and vegetables, bread and sweetmeats, bright apparel and sturdy footwear. Were it not for the noisy scooter that has just roared past, I could be back in the days of Don Orazio G Battista Ravaschieri Fieschi, Prince of Belmonte [1]. Don't be fooled by scenic reminders of a bygone age, though. Italian children today are better educated than those in the UK: all secondary school pupils, whether on the science side (*Liceo Scientifico*) or the arts (*Liceo Classico*), take some science and mathematics right up to school leaving age of 17 or 18.

The English disease
I mentioned C P Snow's 'Two cultures' – that of the Arts and that of the Sciences – in the opening chapter, and concluded that it is not so much a conflict between Arts and Science, as between a well-educated and a poorly-educated person. That difference is particularly acute in Britain, where state education has lagged behind other European countries and the USA since the eighteenth century. The reason is simple: private education in Britain – enjoyed by just 7% of schoolchildren – is so much better than that offered by the state. Yet it is from that 7% that the law-makers emerge.

A quarter of a century has passed since Keith Joseph displayed his ignorance of science at Margaret Thatcher's tea party, described in Chapter 1. Since then, little has changed in regard to science education. John Major's tenure as prime minister did nothing to redress the situation: doubling the number of universities in Britain, by turning polytechnics into universities, merely diluted funds for academic science by pretending that all were of equal calibre. He should have followed the example of California where the two state systems – prestigious University of California (UC) research campuses like Berkeley and UCLA, and excellent California State University (CSU) mainly teaching campuses like Fullerton and San Diego – sit alongside one another in amity [2].

Tony Blair's stated priorities on taking office in 1997 were 'Education, Education and Education'. At last Britain would catch up with the rest of the developed world. Blair and Gordon Brown hurled a quarter of a trillion pounds of tax-payers' money into the system over the next 13 years. What happened? Many schools were refurbished and others rebuilt. But although good classrooms make teaching and learning more agreeable, they do not necessarily lead to better results, any more than a new football stadium or swimming pool guarantees athletic success: the participants play a more decisive role. In fact new school premises achieved little. The education of youngsters in all subjects has declined continuously over the last few decades. In England, a quarter of 11-year-olds are unable to complete a coherent sentence, 10% of boys at that age have the reading skills of a 7-year-old, you don't have to be able to speak a word of French in order to pass GCSE [3] in that subject (it's considered too stressful) and you can obtain an advanced diploma in engineering [4] with zero marks in this, your chosen subject [5].

So children leave school illiterate, and one in five is unemployable: 'It's a disgrace. The politicians have a huge amount to answer for over the past 50 or 60 years' according to Sir Michael Rake, head of British Telecom [6]. Dumbing-down, coupled to political correctness, means that children know more about the problems of gay marriage than about the properties of gaseous molecules. As one disillusioned physics teacher puts it 'I want to teach my subject, to pass on my love of physics to those few who would appreciate it. But I can't. There is nothing to love in the new course. I see no reason that anyone taking this new GCSE would want to pursue the subject. This is the death of physics. My complaints about the new syllabus fall into four categories: the vague, the stupid, the political, and the non-science' and he goes on to give examples of each [7]. Another teacher, who tries valiantly to teach in an inner-city comprehensive (state) school, says 'Britain's state education system is an international disgrace which is incapable of reaching the absurdly low target of pupils achieving five grade Cs at GCSE. Mixed ability teaching, where bright students are taught alongside the less able, is insane because it means no pupils can receive the teaching they require [8]. One report has described the educational system as 'intellectually deficient', and another points out that pupils are not being stretched because of a culture of 'low expectations' [9]. A further reason for poor science teaching is obvious: the calibre of science teachers is among the worst in the developed world [10]. They are also the lowest-paid: aside from new buildings, much of the money poured into the educational system in the UK over the past decade has been spent on devising yet more targets and assessments for the already over-worked teachers to meet and complete. Teaching became only the second of their priorities. So the number of students taking science at university has dropped steadily: 25% fewer read chemistry or physics than a decade ago; a third of physics departments were forced to close between 1994 and 2004 [11]. In Scotland, the educational system may be superior, but science is not at the forefront.

In most of the countries of continental Europe, the situation is better: as I mentioned, children have to take science and mathematics up to school-leaving age. However few of their political leaders are graduates in science. Most have degrees in law or economics. Not surprising then that blame for the scandal of HIV-tainted blood given to haemophiliacs in France during 1984 and 1985 was laid at the hands of the politicians [12]. In the USA, the scientific naivety of Al Gore meant that his crusade against global warming was viewed with more scepticism than it merited (see Chapter 4). Only in China are senior politicians trained in technology. The more didactic approach to teaching science and mathematics follows the jet stream in the northern hemisphere: from west to east. A study in which ability in maths and science is measured in 10-year-olds and 14-year-olds, clearly shows this trend. The USA, England and other European countries are well down the table, whereas Hong Kong, Korea (South), Japan, Singapore and Taiwan are pretty much top of the league. These results, which are compiled every four years, are for 2007 [13]. For earlier years, countries of the former Soviet bloc like the Russian Federation, Hungary and Czech Republic were closely behind the far Eastern nations: communism is not incompatible with effective – if biased – education. Witness countries like Cuba or the Indian state of Kerala. They have benefited from socialism not only in regard to education, but to health as well, since the latter follows the former. Yet science education is suffering across the globe: 450 university science teachers, from 30 countries in Asia, Europe and North America, consider the subject in their country to be 'mediocre, poor or very poor'. The major problem is inadequate science teaching in secondary schools [14].

If more science graduates and fewer lawyers entered politics, the result might be remarkably refreshing. I say 'might', because there are few examples around to confirm my prognosis. It is easy to be dismissive of the scientific artlessness of potential presidential candidates in the USA or of government ministers in the UK. I am referring not just to the BSE crisis described in Chapter 2, but to a Salmonella fiasco precipitated by health minister Edwina Currie in 1988. She caused an outcry among the farming community by saying that 'most of the egg production in this country, sadly, is now affected with Salmonella' [15]. Officials at her Department of Health could not confirm this statement, and the British Egg Industry Council pointed out that the risk of Salmonella in eggs was less than 1 in 200 million. But since more than 30 million eggs were being eaten daily in the UK, it is not surprising that a few people fell ill; no one died.

A quartet of scientifically-trained leaders

Is there any evidence that a scientific education makes a better politician? So far as US presidents are concerned, none appears to have had a university education in science. Jimmy Carter (39th president) attended the US Naval Academy at Annapolis (where he was certainly exposed to some science), followed by Georgia Tech for extra maths. He then served in Admiral Rickover's programme for developing nuclear submarines that I mentioned in Chapter 4. Whatever benefit this may have given him, it did not include a flair for strategic planning, as evidenced by the attempted rescue of 52 Americans held hostage in Iran in 1980.

In contrast Dwight Eisenhower's (34th president) planning ability, and especially his attention to detail, were masterly. They were put to good use in his role as Commander-in-Chief of Overlord, the allied invasion of Normandy in 1944. The qualities may well have been honed through the science taught at West Point Military Academy (remember James McNeill Whistler's projected army career, that ended when he failed chemistry at West Point by writing 'silicon is a gas'). As President, Eisenhower may be criticised for allowing Senator Joseph McCarthy's ludicrous but malign crusade against alleged communists within the United States to go on for as long as it did. Film stars and directors, writers and professors were targeted. Even Secretary of the Army Robert T Stevens was on the Senator's list. Eisenhower bided his time until the scale of the absurdities finally destroyed McCarthy's credibility. Where the President showed decisive action, perhaps prompted by scientific perception, was in dismissing calls from his countrymen to react to the announcement that the Soviet Union had successfully launched a space vehicle ('Sputnik') in 1957. 'The demand for shelters, for more bombers, for more bombs, for more research and development of missiles and satellites, was nearly irresistible. Only Ike could have gotten away with saying no. His unique prestige among his countrymen made (him) unassailable on the question of national defense. ... But Eisenhower said no, and kept saying no to the end of his term. He thereby saved his country untold billions of dollars and no one knows how many war scares. Eisenhower's calm, common-sense, deliberate response to Sputnik may have been his finest gift to the nation, if only because he was the only man who could have given it' [16].

Turning to politicians who received a proper university education in science or medicine, just four spring to mind. Each became their country's prime minister. Three of the four were female. Becoming head of your government and being successful in the job, especially if you are a woman, is no mean achievement. It is therefore clear that every one of those personages is (or was) an outstanding personality. This makes it difficult to discern the contribution of a scientific background. Let me try.

Jan Christian Smuts (1870-1950)

Few young readers of this book, other than South Africans, are likely to have heard of Smuts. My reason for including him in this quartet is that the subjects he read at Victoria College in Stellenbosch (later Stellenbosch University) were Literature and Science, in which he gained double first-class honours. Although he subsequently studied law at Christ's College, Cambridge – again achieving a double first and the rarely bestowed George Long prize in Roman Law and Jurisprudence – his love of science never left him. In 1924 he wrote *Holism and Evolution*, in which he proposed a holistic view of nature: he was probably the first to use this term. Smuts valued an invitation to preside over the Centenary Meeting of the British Association for the Advancement of Science in 1931 as the crowning glory of his life. Einstein judged Smuts to be 'one of only 11 men in the world' who conceptually understood his theory of relativity, and Alexander Todd, Master of Christ's College, Cambridge, in 1970 considered three members of his college to have been truly outstanding: Milton, Darwin and Smuts [17].

Smuts was a born leader, fighting against Britain during the second Boer War and alongside her against Germany and her allies in both world wars (1914-18 and 1939-45, which he lumped together as a modern 'Thirty Years' War'). He was also a politician: twice prime minister of the Union of South Africa (1919-24 and 1939-48), a member of Lloyd George's War Cabinet in the latter stages of World War I and of Winston Churchill's during World War II. In many ways, Smuts' qualities epitomise what I have called 'intellectual leadership' [18].

He has been called the Father of the Constitution (of the Union of South Africa). This came into being in 1910 as a result of merging four entities: the British colonies of Natal and the Cape, and the Republics of Transvaal and the Orange Free State. Smuts was its main author. He drafted the Constitution in true Jeffersonian style: the white population, of Boers and English, would have equal and unalienable rights; the black inhabitants (who outnumbered the whites by 4:1 in South Africa) were swept under the carpet. It is true that Smuts tried to lessen the consequences of Nationalist opinion (that would lead eventually to segregation and apartheid), but in his heart he 'had complete confidence in the intellectual and administrative superiority of the white man' [19]. He would be justly criticised after his death [20] for failing to persuade his colleagues to reach a more moderate resolution of the 'Native problem'.

Drafting the constitution successfully (in the eyes of Europeans) led to his invitation to participate in two further drafts: that of the League of Nations in 1919 and the Charter of the United Nations in 1945. At Versailles in 1919 Smuts, like Woodrow Wilson, foresaw the consequences of Lloyd George's (and Clemenceau's) determination to 'squeeze Germany until the pips squeak'. The peace treaty, Smuts said, '... is not just, and it cannot be durable. Many of the terms are impossible to carry out. They will produce political and economic chaos in Europe for a generation, and in the long run it will be the British Empire that will have to pay the penalty ... This Treaty has been called an English peace, but it is nothing of the sort. The military occupation of a large part of industrial Germany for 15 years is indefensible, from every point of view ... The roots of war are in the document ... When aggression comes ... the British Empire will be called up to jump in.' [21]. A prophetic statement indeed.

So how much did the early scientific training that Smuts received influence his future decisions? On his installation as Chancellor of the University of Cape Town in 1937 (he was Chancellor also of Cambridge University and the recipient of 29 honorary degrees), he told the students that 'to know the world is to get down to a true sense of fact, which remains true in spite of all our opinions and partialities and attitudes' - an entreaty our blinkered politicians the world over would do well to heed. Smuts went on 'This lesson of the true value of fact is perhaps the greatest lesson that science can teach us ...' [22]. His son wrote: 'People are inclined to think of him as a scientist merely in addition to being already a soldier and a politician. Here they are really putting the cart before the horse, for whatever other qualities my father possessed, he was above all a scientist. It was from this attribute he inherited the characteristic of careful analysis – the taking apart of things to discover basic factors and principles. It was from this he inherited a clarity of reasoning and perspective which some have attributed to his legal training ... His clarity of thought and method of reasoning never varied ... he was a good general and a good politician because he was a versatile scientist.' [23]. Clarity of thought and reasoning is something that underlies each of the following politician's decisions also.

Margaret Thatcher (1925-)

The example of Margaret Thatcher does not, at first sight, support my argument very well. In 1985, six years into her premiership, a majority of academics at Oxford refused to approve a motion to confer an honorary degree on her. It was the first time that the university had not accorded this accolade to one of its alumni (she had entered Somerville College, Oxford to read chemistry in 1944) who had become prime minister [24]. The opponents pointed to the cuts in higher education, of which scientific research was a part, that Margaret Thatcher's government had imposed four years earlier. At that time, 364 economists had written a letter to *The Times* criticising the budget. It had 'no basis in economic theory' and would threaten 'social and political stability'. Questioned in the House of Commons whether she could name even two economists in her support, she had cited Patrick Minford and Alan Walters, 'but, it is said, she was relieved not to have been asked to name a third' [25]. A few year later, 'Save British Science' was launched with an advertisement in *The Times* that urged people to ask their member of parliament to 'help to save British science before it is too late ... The government's support for research is declining, falling behind that of our main industrial competitors in Europe ...' [26]. Let us examine Margaret Thatcher's record a little more closely.

As Secretary of State for Education and Science in Edward Heath's administration of 1970-74, she argued against the Chancellor of the Exchequer [27], Anthony Barber. He considered the Open University, that enables adults to access higher education cheaply and to gain degrees, through part-time courses in a number of subjects including scientific ones, as a gimmick of the previous prime minister, Harold Wilson. Barber was intent on abolishing it. Thatcher won, and the Open University has been able to develop its science courses continuously, to the benefit of a huge number of adults who would not otherwise have had the opportunity of a scientific education. It is true that financial support of higher education and science declined during her years as prime minister, but Britain's economy was in bad shape. Five years of labour government under Harold Wilson had forced his chancellor, Denis Healey, to go cap-in-hand to the World Bank to request a loan. Wilson may have talked about the 'white heat of the (scientific and technical) revolution', but it produced little economic return. Thatcher had to reverse Britain's slide into bankruptcy, and this meant cutting back on every aspect of public expenditure, particularly as she espoused the concept of a free market economy. Even so, the basic science budget actually increased by 15% in real terms between 1979 and 1988. The fruits of new policies take time to ripen. During her time as Leader of the Opposition, her mentor in working out how Britain's financial plight could be remedied, had been Keith Joseph. On becoming prime minister in 1979, she appointed him Secretary of State for Education and Science. Joseph's scientific thinking may have been confused, but his views on education were sound.

Joseph was followed as Secretary of State by another non-scientist, Kenneth Baker. Both allowed their civil servants considerable leeway in matters scientific, and needless to say none of the mandarins of the civil service was a scientist. So Thatcher had to fight against the scientifically illiterate views of both her ministers and her civil servants. But fight she did. One area where, in her view, money was being wasted was in the support of industrial research and development. Firms like GEC [28] and Rolls Royce were receiving generous tranches of public money in order to develop technologies that should have been paid for by the profits generated by their respective businesses. She knew what she was talking about. In 1951 she had published a scientific paper [29] while working in the research laboratory of J Lyons & Co. Her studies, that had received no public funds, led to a novel technology: the production of soft frozen ice cream. Hardly as sophisticated as the development of liquid crystals by GEC, but it led to her conviction that supporting the development of products coming out of basic science departments made economic sense, whereas showering industrial laboratories with tax-payers' money did not.

Kenneth Baker wanted the UK to pull out of CERN in 1987. This is a nuclear research facility outside Geneva, set up as *Conseil Européen pour la Recherche Nucléaire* by 11 European countries in 1952. The name changed to *Organisation Européen pour la Recherche Nucléaire* two years later, but the acronym endured. The organisation – now the world's largest particle physics laboratory – provides linear accelerators for the study of fundamental particles. The discovery of W and Z bosons there in 1983 led to a Nobel Prize a year later for the principal investigators Carlo Rubbia and Simon van der Meer. A further Nobel, for Georges Charpak, was to follow in 1992. The financial management structure during the 1980s was weak, and Baker felt that the cost of staying in CERN was not justified. No technologies of potential economic benefit to the UK seemed to be emerging from the institute. Thatcher agreed that better financial control was called for, and she caused the UK to lead in implementing this change. But she was determined that 'the nation as a whole *must* support the discovery of basic scientific knowledge through government finance'. She was aware that 'although basic science can have colossal economic rewards, they are totally unpredictable. And therefore the rewards cannot be judged by immediate results' [30]. Britain remained in CERN.

Margaret Thatcher's background enabled her to understand more effectively what current science was about, and her interest in the latest advances never waned. Ten years into her premiership she invited Britain's top scientists to lunch: 15 Nobel laureates sat down with her at 10 Downing Street (at least one other was prevented by illness from attending). Thatcher thought that university scientists engaged in fundamental research should do more to exploit their discoveries, by taking out potentially lucrative patents. It is true that in the 1980s, corduroy-clad academics had not yet acquired the thirst for notoriety and wealth they were to develop during the following decades. But one man gave the lie to

Thatcher's assumption that academic scientists lacked entrepreneurship. He was Cesar Milstein, the discoverer of monoclonal antibodies (for which he was awarded a Nobel prize). Milstein realised all too well the potentiality of his work, and tried hard to patent the technology. He was let down not by the lack-lustre vision of British companies (who in 1940 had turned down Howard Florey's plea for the large-scale manufacture of penicillin as a result of which this most lucrative of patents finished up in the USA), but by the blinkered approach of the Medical Research Council (MRC). It was this government-funded organisation that refused to let Milstein apply for a patent. Milstein had held off from publishing his results (once disclosed you cannot then apply for a patent in the UK), but the intransigence of the MRC forced his hand. He submitted his work for publication, and another lucrative patent went to the USA, where patent law is different. Gradually it became clear to Margaret Thatcher that it was her own ministries, not the scientists, who were holding up the exploitation of hard-won knowledge.

Margaret Thatcher was one of the first world leaders to recognise the dangers of environmental change; Gro Harlem Brundtland (see below) was the other. By 1988 Thatcher had identified three changes in atmospheric chemistry that had become subjects of concern: an increase in greenhouse gases – carbon dioxide, methane, and chlorofluorocarbons – that was leading to global warming; a large hole in the ozone layer, that protects against ultra-violet radiation from the sun; and acid rain downwind from industrial centres, that was affecting soils, lakes and trees. The first of these is now the centre-piece of everyone's concern. Her government, she said, would espouse 'the concept of *sustainable* economic development' (another prescient comment). 'Stable prosperity can be achieved throughout the world provided the environment is nurtured and safeguarded. Protecting this balance of nature is therefore one of the great challenges of the late twentieth century ...' [30].

It is difficult to find reference to the benefits of Thatcher's scientific background in any of the biographies written about her (including her own). George Guise, Thatcher's science advisor in her policy unit, told me that 'She never discussed the issue of whether her chemistry BA and subsequent BSc helped her as a politician. However she always showed an active interest in scientific matters and it is no exaggeration to say that she and I were the only people in No 10 to whom science was of interest. The rest regarded science as a tiresome bore and science expenditure as a waste of money unless it was going into the likes of GEC or Rolls-Royce to produce something "useful"'. David Willets, another member of Thatcher's policy unit, thought that her training as a scientist meant that 'She was much more rigorous about evidence and facts than most politicians.

The process of speech writing was so slow and anguished because it was deeply serious. She would only consider advice from people after they had been tested on their knowledge of facts and evidence. She would expect us in her policy unit to know the most obscure facts about contribution conditions for a benefit, rules on exemption from prescription charges or obscure tax reliefs' [31]. So Margaret Thatcher's success depended not only on the possession of a sharp intellect and an innate ability to lead, but also to her attention to detail. It is the last of these qualities that is honed through the study of science, and especially through the experience of carrying out a piece of scientific research. A scientific background may not have been the root cause of Thatcher's achievements [32], but it provided the nourishment that enabled her to rise above her peers nationally and internationally. Although François Mitterand told her that she had the 'eyes of Caligula and the mouth of Marilyn Monroe' – not a bad combination for a female politician actually – others have not been so kind [33].

It is true that, like Smuts, Thatcher had her weak moments. Her attention to detail wavered in 1990 when she supported the idea of a poll tax [34] that had been suggested by one of her less able ministers. This error of judgement was one of the factors that led her downfall later that year – precipitated not by the electorate or even by her party, but – as with Caesar – by her peers (the other factor was her stance over the proposed single European currency; in this case her judgement had actually been correct, as became evident 20 years later). Her heir as leader of the Conservative party had an uphill struggle simply to remain in power, and after Tony Blair's spectacular win for Labour in 1997, successive leaders of the Conservative party were to come and go with the regularity of the leap-year cycle for the next 13 years.

Gro Harlem Brundtland (1939-)

In June 2000, a reporter covering the fifth anniversary of the UN Beijing Conference on Women in New York asked five of the women leaders present [35] how it was that they had achieved such prominent positions within the UN system. Catherine Bertini answered for all when she replied that it was because her father had supported and encouraged her (true also of Margaret Thatcher and Angela Merkel). In 1974 Gudmund Harlem, a Norwegian Labour cabinet Minister for 10 years, had told his daughter Gro: ' Yes, you can do it. Accept the challenge' [36] when she was offered the post of Minister of the Environment. So began a political career that would span 30 years.

Gro decided early on that she wanted to be a doctor, and followed in her father's footsteps to read medicine at the University of Oslo. There she met a fellow student, Olav Brundtland. Their engagement was a surprise to many. Olav was a Conservative, while Gro was staunch Labour. Yet their marriage would prove to be one of the most successful of any political leader. Olav became the bedrock on whom Gro could depend – whether looking after their four children or ironing Gro's dress on her way to be appointed Prime Minister by the King. When Henry Kissinger met the Brundtlands in 1981, he commented that 'This would not work in the United States. The press would tear it apart' [37]. Yet there were limits. Olav considered running for parliament as a Conservative in 1981, while Gro was heading a Labour government. In his memoir *Married to Gro*, he states that he thought she would divorce him if he were elected: Gro concurs.

Attending to her medical studies during successive pregnancies had not been easy. While studying for her exams, Gro would breast-feed her son Knut in the ladies' cloakroom of the National Hospital. When her daughter Kaja was born, the baby frequently accompanied her mother on night shifts. Such experiences left their mark on the future politician. As Prime Minister she set in train the opportunity for any parent who needed it to have access to a nursery school for their child. On gaining her medical degree in 1963, Gro spent two years at the Harvard School of Public Health, while Olav was a visiting scholar at the Harvard Center for International Affairs. The training Gro received in ecology, sociology, statistics and epidemiology, to which she then added contagious diseases, psychiatry and internal medicine while serving as deputy superintendent of school health of Oslo, would influence her decisions in public life from then on.

The advantage of a scientific or medical background is not difficult to discern in Gro's case. After being appointed Minister for Environment Affairs by Labour Prime Minister Trygve Bratelli in 1974, a journalist teased her: 'Do you really need a medical degree? As soon as these Harlems reach 30-something, they get drafted into government, always as the youngest member.' (It was a prescient remark: Gro's sister Hanne would follow her father and sister into government, as Minister of Justice, in 2000). Gro's response encapsulates the gist of this chapter: 'Social and political factors alone dictated my choice to study medicine. In my opinion, I am using my education much more effectively as a government Minister than I could have as a doctor' [38]. Although she would have preferred the Ministry of Social Affairs and Health, Gro took her environmental portfolio seriously. Acid rain, from industrial pollution, was a hotly debated issue. A professor of geology thought that concern over this matter was misplaced. The acidic rainwater would be neutralised as soon as it fell on the alkaline earth. Gro studied the scientific evidence in detail and concluded that the professor's contention was nonsense.

In 1977 a blow-out from a drilling platform at the Ekofisk oil field took everyone by surprise. Efforts to cap it failed. The press and the public were up in arms about the ecological damage being caused by the oil leak, which could not be halted. Gro decided to bring in Red Adair and his team from Texas. Eventually they succeeded in capping the leak. It had been a stressful time for her, so early on in her political career. But she coped. A senior reporter wrote: 'Look at her as she takes her place before the cameras, completely at ease and relaxed, lovely as a jewel, nerves and brain cells under complete control. She speaks concisely, always to the point, seriously, but unsentimentally, and yet with a tough optimism that many of her male colleagues from the world of politics might envy her, instead of indulging themselves in a mixture of hysteria and opportunist point-scoring' [39] These remarks seem to encapsulate the benefits of a scientific background and a hospital doctor's experience when facing an emergency.

A year into her ministerial duties, Gro was elected as Deputy Leader of the Labour Party, and two years after that as member of parliament for Oslo. She would take up her seat only after leaving office, as in Norway cabinet ministers do not sit in parliament. Her political future was assured. In 1981 Prime Minister Odvar Nordli decided to retire and hand over to his colleague Rolf Hansen. The intended successor turned the offer down. In his opinion – and to the surprise of many – the post should go to the Deputy Leader of the party. Hansen's view prevailed and Norway had its first female, and youngest, Prime Minister. 'Gro was something completely new at the Prime Minister's office. It was not only that she is a woman. She was glowing with fighting spirit and willingness to work. It seemed that there could be no task so difficult that it would scare her away from taking it on right away with the conviction that she would find a solution' [40]. Two months later Gro was elected party Leader, but not without opposition. The current leader, Reiulf Steen, had implied that Gro was a moderate with right-wing leanings – not genuine Labour, that she was pro-NATO, and that she was a pragmatist, not a visionary. The first two criticisms, certainly, rang true. Even the third could be upheld.

At a Congress of Norwegian Union of Food-Processing Workers in 1981, she said 'It does not make sense to begin with the illusion that the state could simply distribute money to schools, day care, the health sector, private consumption, and all other things on everybody's list of good wishes' [41]. Would that two decades later Gordon Brown, Chancellor and then Prime Minister in the UK, had understood this simple fact. An article in the *Dagbladet* analysed Gro's policy: 'What does she symbolize? She has turned the environment into a political reality and become the symbol for the soft sides of politics in a society dedicated to economic growth. She might attract new voters, and Labour needs them dearly' [42]. The days of Labour government were indeed numbered, and a strong showing by the Conservatives under Kåre Willoch, with the support of the parties of the middle, won the election in October. Gro had been Prime Minister for just eight months. But she would return.

Meanwhile the world beckoned. In 1983 UN Secretary-General Perez de Cuellar asked Gro to head a newly established World Commission on Environment and Development, subsequently known as the Brundtland Commission. Its mission was to consider finance, resources, energy and industry, as well as education, health, and family planning, on a global scale. The findings were stark. First, the use of fossil fuels for energy could not be sustained without affecting the atmosphere. This conclusion led to the Rio de Janeiro Conference on Environment and Development, also known as the Earth Summit, in 1992, and thence to the setting up of the International Panel on Climate Change (IPCC) that I alluded to in Chapter 4. Second, world-wide poverty needed to be addressed, while at the same time stimulating economic growth. The commission considered it possible to achieve a better environment, more health care and education, and a simultaneous reduction in poverty. Noble goals, which are beginning to be fulfilled, if only at a snail's pace. At this time Gro invited Margaret Thatcher to Oslo, to discuss acid rain and sanctions against the apartheid regime in South Africa. They disagreed on both points. Yet the style of the 'Super Woman' of Norway was not dissimilar to that of the 'Iron Lady' of Britain. As a Norwegian union leader put in regard to the former, 'She does not listen to anyone, to no one at all' [43].

By 1985 the Conservative government was teetering, as its supporting parties of the Centre began to lose faith in the policies of tax cuts and public spending without a supporting increase in revenues. Norway's economy, dependent on off-shore oil revenues and the fishing industry, was not doing well. Labour won the election the following year and Gro was Prime Minister once more. But she struggled to reverse Norway's economic decline as world oil prices fell. 'Strong leader for weak government', the *Aftenposten* wrote. 'No one can take away from the Prime Minister that she has been a virtuoso on the untuned instrument that Parliament is for any government. Deep into particulars, she has procured a majority for the policies Labour wants to implement' [44]. Those policies focused largely on educational reforms. Gro increased the time children spent at school by lowering the compulsory starting age from seven to six. On the international front she had one success and one failure. Norway triumphed in its bid to host the 1994 Winter Olympics at Lillehammer, but the prime minister's efforts to persuade her countrymen to join the European Union, as Finland and Sweden had done, was unsuccessful. They preferred to remain part of the wider European Economic Area, together with Iceland and Lichtenstein [45] (they may well have been right). Despite this setback, her leadership did not suffer. 'When this morning ... you had already put behind you the great loss and only were concerned about the future, you gave us all new courage. I for my part had decided to leave politics in the event of a "no" ... Your behaviour last night and this morning made me change my mind. In view of your performance, it became totally unthinkable to jump ship', according to one of her State Secretaries [46].

Labour lost the election of 1989 but was back a year later when a weak Conservative government under Jan Syse collapsed. Gro's policies on strengthening education, health and women's role in public life, continued. She could proudly point to the fact that a quarter of Norway's work force was now in the public sector (fine, but a ratio of more than 50%, as at the end of the UK Labour Party's years in power in 2010, is surely unsustainable). Labour lost the election of 1996, but Gro was not done yet. At 57 years of age, her early medical training would reach its ultimate fulfilment. Several international positions were being mooted by her supporters: Secretary-General of NATO, a new post of Deputy Secretary-General to Kofi Annan at the United Nations that was likely to lead to Secretary-General itself, and Director-General of the World Health Organisation. The last took her fancy, but did not land in her lap without considerable lobbying by Gro herself over more than a year. She travelled to Angola, Bhutan, Botswana, Egypt, the Gulf States, Sri Lanka, Tanzania and Zimbabwe, as she was particularly keen to garner the votes of Executive Board members from developing countries. She succeeded and won 18 of the 34 votes, a clear majority. As WHO's first woman Director-General, she became also the first feminine head of any UN organisation.

At WHO, Gro's innovations were far reaching. She initiated a cabinet of Executive Directors, each of whom would have responsibility for a specific facet of the organisation's mission. She promoted opposition to the tobacco industry and an emphasis on mental illness. Her youngest son's suicide in 1992 was surely not without influence on the latter objective. Two research programmes were launched in regard to infectious diseases that afflict the poorest countries of the world: Roll Back Malaria, and the Stop TB Initiative. Both continue to support the development of new therapies for diseases that currently kill more than two million people a year, mainly children under five in regard to malaria.

Gro Harlem Brundtland's words speak for themselves, in so far as my contention that leaders benefit from a scientific or medical education is concerned: 'My training in public health has guided me as a politician. ... As a doctor and as a politician, you have to first ask: What is the problem? Then, how can we prevent and cure this problem? Who needs to become involved? How shall we act together to reach common goals? Answering these questions is what I have done all my life' [47].

Angela Merkel (1954-)

Angela Merkel is still very much in office, so it may be thought premature to consider her political achievements in terms of her scientific training. Yet some indications are already apparent. Gro Harlem Brundtland may have been called the fourth most influential European (behind Pope John Paul II, Mikhail Gorbachev and Margaret Thatcher) by the *Financial Times* in 2004; Angela Merkel was rated number one of the World's One Hundred Most Powerful Women for each of the last five years by *Forbes* magazine. Like Gro, whose family had to flee to neutral Sweden in 1943 (her father's work for the Norwegian resistance had become known to the Nazi authorities), Angela's early childhood suffered a family move: in her case, from benign West Germany to the ruthless DDR (German Democratic Republic or East Germany). Shortly after the birth of his daughter Angela, pastor Horst Kasner was transferred to a Lutheran congregation in Brandenburg and the family moved to Templin, north of Berlin in the East Zone. Angela remained in the DDR throughout its existence.

She studied physics at the University of Leipzig, followed by two years in the Central Institute for Physical Chemistry of the Academy of Sciences in Berlin-Adlershof. Upon completion of her doctoral thesis in quantum chemistry, her thoughts turned to politics. She became deputy spokesperson in the caretaker government of Lothar de Maizière, and in the first general election after unification in 1990, entered the Bundestag (parliament) as member for Stralsund and surrounding districts in east Germany, which she has represented ever since. The following year Chancellor Helmut Kohl appointed Merkel as his Minister for Women and Youth, and in 1994 as Minister for the Environment, Nature Conservation and Nuclear Safety; she remained the youngest member of his cabinet. So her political career started rather as Gro's did, and would continue in the same vein, except for the colour of her political affiliation: Christian Democrat (conservative), not Socialist.

During her time as Environment Minister, Merkel summarised her views in an article entitled 'The role of science in sustainable development'. She writes that 'The key aim for the twenty-first century is "sustainable development," which the international community embraced at the 1992 UN Conference on Environment and Development' (that emanated from the Brundtland Commission). 'Sustainable development seeks to reconcile environmental protection and development; it means nothing more than using resources no faster than they can regenerate themselves, and releasing pollutants to no greater extent than natural resources can assimilate them. If we are to move toward sustainable development, the industrialized countries will have to accept special responsibility – not only because of their past ecological sins, but also because of their present technological know-how and financial resources. ... The German government has chosen the socio-ecological market economy as the framework for shaping production and consumption in keeping with sustainable development, while at the same time encouraging innovation in industry and society. The key is to sever the traditional link between economic growth and the consumption of resources, which increasingly threatens the natural basis for life and the preservation of natural and landscape diversity.

'There are several possible ways to achieve environmental compatibility in lifestyles and economies. Technical and scientific innovations provide excellent prospects for environmental protection. As we approach the end of the twentieth century, industrial society is becoming a knowledge-based society. It is vital that we use our growing knowledge and capabilities responsibly, and that we use them in the interest of environmentally appropriate development. Science must play an important role in the pursuit of sustainable development ... Sustainability, as a strategic aim, involves optimizing the interactions between nature, society, and the economy, in accordance with ecological criteria. Political leaders and scientists alike face the challenge of recognizing interrelationships and interactions between ecological, economic, and social factors and taking account of these factors when seeking solution strategies. To meet this challenge, decision-makers require interdisciplinary approaches and strategies that cut across political lines. Environmental discussions must become more objective, and this includes, especially, debates about the risks of new technologies, which are often ideologically charged. In light of the complex issues involved in sustainable development, we need clearer standards for orienting and assessing our environmental policies ...' [48]. The scientific background of all three lady prime ministers – Thatcher, Brundtland and Merkel – has surely been of significance in leading them to focus on the same global problem.

In Germany, as in Norway, single parties rarely have a mandate to rule. Successive governments have to rely on coalitions with minor parties. So despite the fact that Merkel was elected Secretary-General, later leader, of the CDU (Christian Democratic Union) on Kohl's defeat in the 1998 election, she would have to ally herself with the CSU (Christian Social Union), that is dominated by Catholic Bavarians. Perhaps I may remind readers that Germany's first unification occurred in the nineteenth century (1990 merely saw the re-unification of the west with the east). Prior to 1871 the country was divided roughly north-south on largely religious lines. Ever since Martin Luther's time, Saxony, Prussia and adjacent states in the north have been predominantly Protestant, whereas Bavaria in the south retained its Catholic links with the Holy Roman Empire (Austro-Hungarian Empire until the end of the first world war).

Angela Merkel, in common with many members of the CDU, is a staunch Protestant. In order to defeat the SDP (Social Democratic Party) that had gained power in 1998 under Gerhard Schröder in alliance with the Green Party, she had to endure endless shenanigans between CDU and CSU. But she persevered in her opposition to Schröder's policies of anti-Americanism, anti-nuclear power and pro-Turkish accession to the European Union. This found sufficient favour with the German people to lead to her winning the election of 2005. She was now Germany's first female Chancellor.

The qualities that have led to Angela Merkel's achievements have been evaluated by Gerd Langguth in the form of 12 interrelated 'theses'. First, 'she shares with Kohl and Schröder the undeniable will to power.' Second, 'the ideology-free scientist Merkel is a generalist without a fixation on history ... her political viewpoint is formed from the rationality of a scientist', but 'a scientific-mechanistic viewpoint of politics easily underestimates traditional attitudes and interests of people – their emotions.' Third, 'her life has been stamped by her relationship with her father.' Fourth, 'as a citizen of the DDR, she learnt early on to separate her private thoughts from the official world of loyalty to the state.' Fifth, as a result of her experience of life in the DDR and of Marxist-Leninism, 'she thinks in terms of individual freedom and responsibility: from that springs her positive view of America.' Sixth, 'Merkel is sceptical of all that stems from regulation of society. "Doubt leads to freedom" could be her motto.' Seventh, 'Merkel's stance in regard to political goals equates more to rational insight than to traditional Christian Democrat viewpoints.' Eighth, her 'perception of women in continuously male-dominated politics is relentless and without reservation ... Merkel's view of women distances her from (other) West German female politicians.' Ninth, 'Merkel embodies all-German history as no one before her. As chancellor her East German upbringing serves her well.' Tenth, 'Angela Merkel became chancellor because she, as no other politician, recognised her chance, and to realise it she accepted every risk.' Eleventh, 'more than all her predecessors, Angela Merkel works with the media to influence people's minds' (a legacy from her DDR days?). Finally, 'as chancellor, Angela Merkel found her leitmotif with climate change. Her pragmatic outlook towards politics makes ruling with various coalitions possible. ... She can win or lose all. So far she has won all' [49].

Another author, Matthias Krauss, analyses the media's assessment of Merkel. *Der Stern* believes that her scientific background makes her 'a physicist with power', *Die Wirtschaftswoche* considers her to be 'a restless elementary particle', while *Die Welt* ascribes a 'grain of physics' to her personality. 'Merkel calls her stance "Politics without lies"'. To Krauss 'that sounds presumptive, but has its origin in being educated in physics. Self-deception is the beginning of the end'. *Das*

Handelsblatt considers her to be the 'Sphinx without secrets' [50]. Then there is her upbringing under communism: 'Angela Merkel has succeeded not despite the fact that grew up in the DDR, but *because* she was a child of that state' [51]. Dirk Kurbjuweit, bureau chief of *Der Spiegel*, 'values her for her intelligence and her humour', even though she 'has never made a memorable speech (the fact that this is true of Kohl and Schröder also is beside the point)' [52].

So far as her independence is concerned, she may have been Kohl's protégé, but 'she is neither Kohl's maiden, nor the Machiavella of Mecklenburg' (another attribute in relation to her evident scheming) [53]. What are apparent weaknesses are also the source of her strength, according to Margaret Heckel, author of the best-selling *So regiert die Kanzlerin (How the Chancellor Rules)*: 'She waits so long before she decides, but she is that rare politician who has all the possibilities figured out ahead of her opponents. She analyses how her opponents will react. Then she works out scenarios and her preferred outcome. If she doesn't get there at first count, she tries another route. It is the physicist in her: she uses the trial-and-error method of a scientist' [54]. During the Greek bail-out crisis in the summer of 2011, Angela Markel refused to attend any emergency summit meeting until there was a chance of agreement among the European leaders. And then she largely got her way. However she still has work to do.

I rest my case in regard to the benefit that a scientific training has made to Angela Merkel's success as a politician and world leader.

Removing the blinkers: science education for all

The solution to the problems outlined in this book is obvious. It is no longer acceptable to educate young children merely in reading, writing and arithmetic – the 'three Rs' of former generations. Science needs to be taught alongside these subjects from the earliest age onwards. As C P Snow of the Two Cultures himself realised, 'There is only one way out of all this; it is, of course, by rethinking our education' [55]. Although the need is particularly great in the UK, it applies to a lesser extent throughout continental Europe and the United States. And should not the children of Dhaka and Dar Es Salaam, of Cuernavaco and Caracas, receive the benefits of an education fit for the twenty-first century? Eradication of poverty and resulting disease may constitute a more immediate want, but a scientifically literate child is more able to survive, and may grow up to become a statesman with the necessary vision for change. A new approach to education throughout the world is required. Europe for long led the way: it could do so again. But please, not through edicts from the European Union: the blinkered mandarins of Brussels are simply not up to the job. I have shown what an enlightened leader in a country like Norway can achieve. It is from individual states that change should come. The way forward is by example, not diktat. Agriculture spread naturally out of Mesopotamia and Egypt 10 thousand years ago, the architecture of Florence and Rome washed into neighbouring states during the Renaissance, the English steam engine soon puffed its way across continental Europe, and the United States looked to ancient Athens and Rome (not to Britain) for the symbols of its constitution. Perhaps over the next few decades we can initiate a universal schooling in science from the age of six that will be the envy of the American Republic.

To initiate such change will not be easy, for where are the instructors to carry out this undertaking? We cannot begin the task until teaching in science is made more attractive. The then-head of Pearson, one of the largest enterprises in the UK, gave me a simple answer: 'Pay science teachers double that earned by others'. A teacher of science in primary school should have the same status as paediatrician. What might young pupils learn? Children like books about animals dressed and acting as humans, even though they are fully aware that the rabbits and squirrels, dogs and pigs that they see do not converse with each other. Fables are an important educational tool. My six-year old granddaughter particularly enjoys animal books that contain what she calls 'facts' – such as those that the admirable Nicola Davies, zoologist and author, inserts into her animal stories. In a story about a polar bear, for example, the narrative is not interrupted, but in corners of the pictures are statements such as 'Only a polar bear's nose and the pads on the ends of its toes are without fur'; 'Polar bears' fat keeps them warm in the sea. Webbed feet help them to swim and water-shedding fur helps them to dry off quickly afterwards'; 'In the Arctic it's light all the time in the summer and dark all the time in winter'; 'When the sea ice melts in summer, polar bears can't catch seals. They'll eat almost anything else instead: fish, dead birds, berries, even grass'; 'Scientists think that when humans came to the Arctic, about 40,000 years ago, they learned how to survive by watching polar bears'. My granddaughter loves these bits of information. She is ready for science.

This is the moment when an enlightened teacher might tell her charges that many years ago there were no houses in which to live, and that many, many, many years ago there was no grass on which to sit – but then there were no animals or people to do so anyway. Just rocks. Which is the situation on the moon or on Mars. She might tell them that daylight comes from the sun, and that when they look up at the sky on a clear night, the thousands of twinkling stars that they see are nothing but more suns, just like ours. And so on. Many enlightened nursery (pre-school) teachers, of course, already do this. In Germany, eight-year olds are being taught probabilistic reasoning – the theory of risk (see Chapter 2) – with toys. 'In most parts of the world, children are taught the mathematics of certainty, not uncertainty' [56]. In Norway, as I mentioned in regard to the measures brought in by Gro Harlem Brundtland during her period as prime minister, free education for all now starts at the age of six, and science is part of the curriculum (though not as a separate subject) for the next 10 years. Thereafter all students (aged 16 to 19) are entitled to free education in General Studies or Vocational Studies. Science as such is not a compulsory part of either of these courses, but as Marianne Ødegaard of the Institute for Educational Research at the University of Oslo told me in regard to teaching science over the entire 10+3 years, 'We do not have science as a basic skill. My view point is that argumentation and/or inquiry, which are important skills in science, could be productive basic skills in all subjects' and she's right.

At present many secondary school and university students turn away from science because there are so many boring facts to learn. When I set up a course in biochemistry for medical students at the newly created medical school of St George's Hospital in south London 30 years ago, I received two comments. Each was from a leader in his field. One I ignored, the other I took to heart. The first was from the chairman of the faculty of biochemistry at London University (a federal university, like the University of California, comprising some dozen colleges and medical schools). He said, following the third-year examinations in pre-clinical subjects, 'Do you realise that your students don't know the difference between hexokinase and glucokinase [57]?' 'They don't know the difference because I told them not to bother', I responded. Such detail seemed to me unnecessary for the students' ultimate success at repairing a hernia, advising a worried lady about her eczema, or sitting in the psychiatrist's chair. But I did show our students a three-dimensional model of the protein insulin, to indicate the complexity of the molecules they would have to deal with when confronting a diabetic patient or treating someone in shock. I even wrote a text book [58].

The second was a piece of advice from the chairman of medicine at St George's. 'Most of the biochemistry that you will teach the students will be forgotten by the time they begin their clinical studies. Try to teach them general mechanisms rather than specific facts.' He was right, and it has been the focus of my philosophy as an educator. Others agree. World-class scientist and Nobel laureate Sir Tim Hunt says 'I loved Chemistry in particular, largely because the teacher, Colonel Simmons, was much more concerned with principles than facts, although a thoroughly practical man himself. We were allowed considerable freedom, and on more than one occasion started fires from distilling volatile flammable solvents. One became adept at avoiding injury'. I can vouch for those comments, as I was taught by the admirable Colonel at Magdalen College School, Oxford, myself some years earlier.

Returning to secondary education, who will teach the teachers? What I am proposing is a slow process, that will take a generation or two (25 to 50 years) to achieve. Ensuring universal knowledge of the 'three Rs' during the nineteenth and twentieth centuries took considerably longer. In a democracy, even a couple of generations implies several administrations. The necessary change can therefore come about only if supported by political parties of every hue. It will not be costly. An increase in teaching salaries is a drop in the ocean compared with the proposed costs of moving to a non-carbon economy through gimmicks like wind turbines. Were our politicians not scientifically illiterate, they would realise that nuclear energy (whether by fission or by fusion) is the long-term alternative to fossil fuels. So educating legislators is a cost-saving exercise in the long term. I am not proposing global consensus by compulsion. As I have implied, nations should be free to adopt the transition to a 'three Rs and an S' policy of education as they wish. Evolution within societies may be a slower process than revolution, but it is a preferable one. No one forced hygiene on people over the centuries. Once they saw the benefits, they adopted it (and continue to do so in the developing world) [59]. But we have to make a start. It is time to begin the process of creating an un-blinkered society: from a core of enlightened lawmakers (who I hope are reading this book) to teachers, from teachers to youngsters, and from youngsters when mature, back into an increasing circle of enlightened lawmakers.

My proposal for an immediate measure is the following. Every school – large or small – should set aside a period of half an hour or so once a week for 'scientific assembly'. Everyone should attend, rather like they do for 'religious assembly' in certain schools. Teachers, too, should be encouraged to participate in scientific assembly. Under no circumstance should 'politically correct' head teachers replace religious assembly with scientific assembly. They are not interchangeable: the former nurtures souls, the latter enriches the mind. The head of science should then explain anything of interest that caught his or her eye over the past week, and respond to any questions and comments that are raised. If there is no appropriate person to take on this role, schools should engage a university scientist, from a pool of qualified communicators, to do so; physical science might alternate with biological and medical science as a weekly topic. You might say that a teacher summarising the science section of a weekly newspaper would achieve the same result; but as I have pointed out elsewhere in this book, the media cannot be trusted to always get the science right. What I am suggesting is akin to the situation that existed in the former Soviet Union: every school (institution, factory, military regiment and so forth) had its political 'advisor' to make sure that Bolshevik dogma was being followed. I propose that every school has a scientific 'advisor' to ensure that youngsters are not misled by false notions, but are given the opportunity to absorb novel and interesting scientific findings and to engage in debate about them. None of this costs a great deal in either time or money.

We need also to tackle the problem of scientific ignorance in specific professions. 'Many students who spent much of their life avoiding statistics and psychology become lawyers. Out of some 175 accredited law schools in the United States, only one requires a course in basic statistics or research methods. ... students (at one of the top law schools) who excelled in critical thinking could not evaluate whether a conclusion drawn from statistical evidence was correct or incorrect. ... The courts tend to call in expert witnesses, but ... the experts that courts select can have clouded minds themselves' [60], a situation I illustrated in Chapter 2. Law schools need to include courses in probability and risk. These should also be included in the curriculum for teachers, politicians [61] and journalists

I have indicated that in Britain, at least, science education is deteriorating because of dumbing-down decreed by academics in charge of the curriculum. They may know some science, but government ministers (who don't) force their hand. That is why, throughout this book, I have thrown darts at blinkered politicians, administrators and journalists, as well as an occasional fusillade at scientists who evade the evidence; self-styled atheists, too, have come under attack on account of their blinkered attitude towards history and human sentiment. James Lovelock, proponent of the Gaia hypothesis, and an astute scientist, concurs: 'We live at a time when emotions and feelings count more than truth, and there is a vast ignorance of science' [62].

'Every great age has been shaped by intellectuals of the stamp of Hobbes, Locke, Berkeley, Leibnitz, Voltaire, Montesquieu, Rousseau, Kant, Jefferson and Franklin – all of whom would have been horrified by the proposition that cultivated men and women could dispense with a good grasp of the scientific aspect of the contemporary world picture' according to a comment half a century ago [63]. That is the crux of my argument today. I don't expect the Secretary-General of the United Nations, the Presidents of China, Russia and the USA, ministers of education, energy, health and science in Belgium and Britain, Bangladesh and Brazil, to be familiar with quantum mechanics, the intricacies of immunology or the chemistry of combustion. I do wish, though, that they would understand the difference between conjecture and certainty, between myth and fact, between nuclear fission and nuclear fusion, between a virus and a bacterium, between carbon dioxide produced by man and that by nature [64].

In this Chapter I have focussed primarily on the defects of scientific education in Britain, where the problem is most acute. But it also applies, in lesser measure, to the rest of Europe, North America and beyond. The message is clear. In order to produce well-rounded citizens and informed decision-makers, we need to encourage more young people into science. To enthuse the youth of the world with the passion of their forebears: of a Gregor Mendel, Karl Landsteiner or Konrad Lorenz in Austria, an Isaac Newton, Michael Faraday or Francis Crick in Britain, a Tycho Brahe, Niels Bohr or Jens Skou in Denmark, an Antoine Lavoisier, Louis Pasteur or Jacques Monod in France, an Alexander von Humboldt, Rudolf Virchow or Paul Ehrlich in Germany, a C V Raman, Gobind Khorana or Venkatraman Ramakrishnan in India, a Galileo Galilei, Camillo Golgi or Rita Levi-Montalcini in Italy, a Jacobus van't Hoff, Hendrik Lorentz or Paul Creutzen in the Netherlands, a Nicolaus Copernicus, Maria Sklodowska (Marie Curie) or Kazimierz Funk in Poland, a Dmitri Mendeleev, Ivan Pavlov or Vitaly Ginzburg in Russia, an Oswaldo Cruz, Bernardo Houssay or Luis Leloir in South America, a Ramon y Cajal, Severo Ochoa or Margarita Salas in Spain, a Svante Arrhenius, Arne Tiselius or Bengt Samuelsson in Sweden, an Alfred Werner, Paul Karrer or Kurt Wüthrich in Switzerland, a Benjamin Franklin, Linus Pauling or Richard Feynman in the USA [65]. Who knows, by the turn of this century we may yet recapture the intellectual rigour of the eighteenth.

Notes

[1]   Actually in Don Orazio's time of the seventeenth century, the waves of the Tyrrhenian sea washed right up against the ramparts of the old town. Only during the nineteenth century, it appears, did the salty waters begin to retreat, allowing citrus groves to flourish. As the population gradually increased, lemon trees gave way to dwellings and the modern town of Amantea emerged. If global warming is as extensive as predicted, the sea may once more fill the handsome bay

[2]   See, eg, Charles Pasternak: What is scholarship in the 21st century? The ideas of a university. In *Can the prizes still glitter? The future of British universities in a changing world* (ed Hugo de Burgh, Anna Fazackerley and Jeremy Black, University of Buckingham Press, Buckingham, 2007) pp 81-86

[3]   General Certificate of Secondary Education, taken at around 14-16 years of age

[4] Worth three-and-a-half A levels – the Advanced Level Certificate of Education – that is generally taken between the ages of 16-18

[5] Provided you do well enough in your project, that is marked by your teachers, not by independent examiners

[6] *Daily Telegraph* June 28, 2010

[7] Taken from an open letter to the AQA (Assessment and Qualification Alliance, that organises the exams taken by most students in the UK) – and the Department for Education: *A physics teacher begs for his subject back*

[8] *Sunday Telegraph* October 10, 2010

[9] *Daily Telegraph* December 1, 2009

[10] David Burghes, John Howson, John Marenbon, John O'Leary and Chris Woodhead: *Teachers Matters: Recruitment, Employment and Retention at Home and Abroad* (ed Sheila Lawlor, Politeia, July 2009); see http://www.politeia.co.uk/p97.shtml

[11] Since the decline started under a Conservative administration, Labour alone cannot be blamed for it

[12] Anne-Marie Casteret (1992). *L'affaire du sang.* (Éditions La Découverte, Paris, 1992)

[13] Trends in International Mathematics and Science Study (TIMSS), prepared by the International Center for Education Statistics, part of the US Department of Education; see http://nces.ed.gov/timss/

[14] *Nature* 465: 525-6, 2010

[15] www.bbc.co.uk : BBC News, 3 December 1988

[16] Stephen E Ambrose: *Eisenhower. Soldier and President* (Simon and Schuster, New York, 1990) p 454

[17] F S Crafford: *Jan Smuts: A Biography* (Doubleday, Doran & co, Garden City, NY, 1943) p 140

[18] Charles Pasternak: *Intellectual Leadership: Plato's Dream, Popper's Nightmare* (The Advocate, CUNY Graduate Center, October 2009)

[19] J C Smuts (the son of Smuts): *Jan Christian Smuts.* (Cassell & Company Ltd, London, 1952), p 307

[20] Bernard Friedman: *Smuts. A Reappraisal* (George Allen & Unwin Ltd, London, 1975)

[21] T J Haarhoff: *Smuts. The Humanist. A Personal Reminiscence* (Basil Blackwell, Oxford, 1970), p 93

[22] J C Smuts, p 366

[23] J C Smuts, p 329

[24] At the time of writing, Tony Blair is still waiting for his Hon DCL. Of the 13 prime ministers since World War II, nine (Attlee, Eden, Macmillan, Douglas-Home, Wilson, Heath, Thatcher, Blair, Cameron) were educated at Oxford; of the four who were not (Churchill, Callaghan, Major and Brown), only the last received a university education (at Edinburgh)

[25] Terence Kealey: *Sex, Science and Profits* (William Heinemann, London, 2008), p 337

[26] *The Times*, January 13, 1986

[27] ie finance minister

[28] General Electric Company; not to be confused with the American company, General Electric

[29] H H G Jellinek and M H Roberts: The saponification of α-monostearin in a monolayer *J. Sci. Food Agric.* 2: 391-395, 1951

[30] Excerpt from a speech at a Royal Society dinner on 27 September 1988

[31] David Willetts: *The meaning of Margaret* (Prospect May 2009, pp 32-36)

[32] Her greatest legacy is her economic transformation of Britain during the 1980s, by curbing the malign effect that trade union power was having on the country: it had brought down the Heath government in 1974, curbed Wilson's ability to govern thereafter, and caused Callaghan's defeat in 1979

[33] http://www.guardian.co.uk/politics/2009/apr/11/germaine-greer-margaret-thatcher-anniversary

[34] Officially the Community Charge

[35] Carol Bellamy, Director-General of UNICEF; Catherine Bertini, chair of the UN Standing Committee on Nutrition; Gro Harlem Brundtland, Director General of WHO; Mary Robinson, High Commissioner for Human Rights; Dr Nafis Sadik, leader of the World Population Fund

[36] Gro Harlem Brundtland: *Madam Prime Minister. A Life in Power and Politics* (Farrar, Straus and Giroux, New York, 2002) p 68

[37] Gro Harlem Brundtland, p 147

[38] Gro Harlem Brundtland, p 84

[39] Gro Harlem Brundtland, p 100

[40] According to Wiktor Martinsen, State Secretary for public relations: Gro Harlem Brundtland, p 138

[41] Gro Harlem Brundtland, p 154

[42] Gro Harlem Brundtland, p 142

[43] Gro Harlem Brundtland, p 175

[44] Gro Harlem Brundtland, p 276

[45] The EEA comprises these three countries, plus the European Union; Switzerland is not a member

[46]   Gro Harlem Brundtland, p 333

[47]   Gro Harlem Brundtland, p 471

[48]   Taken from *Science* 281: 336-7, 1998

[49]   Gerd Langguth: *Angela Merkel. Aufstieg zur Macht. Biografie* (Deutscher Taschenbuch Verlag, Munich, 2008), pp 391-424; my translations

[50]   Matthias Krauss: *Das Mädchen für alles. Angela Merkel – ein Annäherungsversuch* (Anderbeck Verlag, 2005), pp 171 & 172; my translations

[51]   Ibid, p192.

[52]   Dirk Kurbjuweit: *Angela Merkel. Die Kanzlerin für alle?* (Carl Hanser Verlag, Munich, 2009) pp 13 & 53; my translations

[53]   Gerd Langguth, p 386. See Bibliography

[54]   From Quentin Peel: *Merkel's nail-biter.* Financial Times June 28, 2010

[55]   C P Snow: *The Two Cultures and the Scientific Revolution. The Rede Lecture, 1959* (Cambridge University Press, Cambridge, 1959), p 18

[56]   *Nature* 461: 1189-92, 2009

[57]   Two different enzymes – ie proteins – that catalyse the same reaction: the addition of a phosphate group to a sugar during metabolism; the first enzyme is non-specific, reacting with any 6-carbon sugar, the second is specific for glucose

[58]   Charles Pasternak: *Introduction to Human Biochemistry* (Oxford University Press, Oxford, 1979)

[59]   One of the greatest social changes during my lifetime – almost comparable to the introduction of mobile telephones or the internet – has been in the cleanliness of lavatories in bars, restaurants and public places in Mediterranean countries like Italy and Spain. The introduction of deodorants is another

[60] Gerd Gigerenzer: *Reckoning with Risk. Learning to live with uncertainty* (Allen Lane: The Penguin Press, London, 2002), p 159

[61] The recently-launched Blavatnik School of Government at Oxford University (http://www.ox.ac.uk/media/news_stories/2010/100920.html) might well include such courses in its curriculum

[62] From David J.C. MacKay: *Sustainable Energy – without the hot air.* (UIT Cambridge, 2008) p 3

[63] George B de Huszar (ed) *The Intellectuals. A Controversial Portrait* (The Free Press of Glencoe, Illinois/George Allen & Unwin, London, 1960), p 190

[64] Most of the carbon dioxide generated by nature is in the ocean, not the atmosphere; note also that plants, trees, grass and plankton release carbon dioxide at night, though this is more than compensated by the absorption of carbon dioxide during daylight

[65] I have deliberately omitted the enlightened Far East and Australasia

Bibliography

John Adams: *Risk* (UCL Press, London, 1995)

Alun Anderson: *After the Ice: Life, Death and Politics in the New Arctic* (Virgin Books, London, 2009)

Jensine Andresen (ed): *Religion in Mind. Cognitive Perspectives on Religious Belief, Ritual, and Experience* (Cambridge U Press, Cambridge, 2001)

Karen Armstrong: *The Great Transformation: The World in the Time of Buddha, Socrates, Confucius and Jeremiah* (Atlantic Books, London, 2006)

Karen Armstrong: *The Case for God. What Religion Really Means* (The Bodley Head, London, 2009)

R Barker Bausell: *Snake Oil Science. The Truth About Complementary and Alternative Medicine* (Oxford U Press, NY, 2007)

A C Benson (ed): *Cambridge Essays on Education* (Cambridge University Press, 1917)

Herbert Benson with Miriam Z Klipper: *The Relaxation Response* (Collins, Fount Paperbacks, London, 1976)

Herbert Benson with William Proctor: *Beyond the Relaxation Response. How to Harness the Healing Power of Your Personal Beliefs* (Collins, Fount Paperbacks, London, 1985)

Christopher Booker and Richard North: *The Great Deception. A Secret History of the European Union* (Continuum, London, 2003)

Christopher Booker and Richard North: *Scared to Death. From BSE to Global Warming – How Scares Are Costing Us the Earth* (Continuum, London, 2007)

Joan Borysenko: *Seven Paths to God. The Ways of the Mystic* (Hay House Inc, Carlsbad, CA, 1997)

Gro Harlem Brundtland: *Madam Prime Minister. A Life in Power and Politics* (Farrar, Straus and Giroux, New York, 2002)

Georges Charpak and Henri Broch: *Debunked! ESP, Telekinesis, and Other Pseudoscience* (trans from the original French by Bart K Holland. Johns Hopkins U Press, Baltimore, MD, 2004)

Deepak Chopra: *Quantum Healing. Exploring the frontiers of mind/body medicine* (Bantam Books, NY, 1989)

Richard Cohen: *Chasing the Sun. The Epic Story of the Star That Gives Us Life* (Simon & Schuster, London, 2010)

Francis Collins: *The Language of God. A Scientist Presents Evidence for Belief* (Simon & Schuster, London, 2007)

Paul Davies: *The Goldilocks Enigma. Why is the universe just right for life?* (Allen Lane, London, 2006)

Richard Dawkins: *The God Delusion* (paperback edition, Black Swan, London, 2007)

Daniel C Dennett: *Breaking the Spell. Religion as a Natural Phenomenon* (Allen Lane, London, 2006)

Robin Dunbar: *How Many Friends Does One Person Need? Dunbar's Number and Other Evolutionary Quirks* (Faber and Faber, London, 2010)

Dylan Evans: *Placebo. The Belief Effect* (HarperCollins, London, 2003)

G R Evans: *Belief. A Short History For Today* (I B Tauris, London, 2006)

Bernard Friedman: *Smuts. A Reappraisal* (George Allen & Unwin, London, 1975)

George Gardiner: *Margaret Thatcher. From Childhood to Leadership* (William Kimber, London, 1975)

Hannah Gay: *The History of Imperial College London 1907-2007. Higher Education and Research in Science, Technology and Medicine* (Imperial College Press, London, 2007)

Gerd Gigerenzer: *Reckoning with Risk. Learning to live with uncertainty* (Allen Lane: The Penguin Press, London, 2002)

Gerd Gigerenzer: *Gut Feelings. The intelligence of the unconscious* (Allen Lane, London, 2007)

Al Gore: *An Inconvenient Truth. The planetary emergency of global warming and what you can do about it* (Bloomsbury, London, 2006)

Andy Green: *Education and State Formation. The Rise of Education Systems in England, France and the USA* (Macmillan, Basingstoke, 1990)

T J Haarhoff: *Smuts. The Humanist. A Personal Reminiscence* (Basil Blackwell, Oxford, 1970)

John Haldane (ed): *Cambridge Essays Values, Education and the Human World. Essays on Education, Culture, Politics, Religion and Science* (Imprint Academic, Exeter, UK 2004)

Sam Harris: *The End of Faith. Religion, Terror, and the Future of Reason* (Free Press, London, 2005)

Sam Harris: *Letter to a Christian Nation* (Bantam Press, London, 2007)

James Harrison (ed): *Scientists as Writers* (Methuen, London, 1965)

Christopher Hitchens: *God is not Great. How Religion Poisons Everything* (Twelve Books, New York, 2007)

Richard Holmes: *The Age of Wonder. How the Romantic Generation Discovered the Beauty and Terror of Science* (Harper Press, London, 2008)

T L Jarman: *Europe Landmarks in the History of Education. English Education as part of the European Tradition* (2nd edn John Murray, London, 1963)

Terence Kealey: *Sex, Science and Profits* (William Heinemann, London, 2008)

Matthias Krauss: *Das Mädchen für alles. Angela Merkel – ein Annäherungsversuch* (Anderbeck Verlag, 2005)

Dirk Kurbjuweit: *Angela Merkel. Die Kanzlerin für alle?* (Carl Hanser Verlag, Munich, 2009)

Nick Lane: *A Life Ascending. The Ten Great Inventions of Evolution* (Profile Books, London, 2010)

Gerd Langguth: *Angela Merkel. Aufstieg zur Macht. Biografie* (Deutscher Taschenbuch Verlag, Munich, 2008)

Nigel Lawson: *An Appeal to Reason. A Cool Look at Global Warming* (Duckworth Overlook, London, 2008)

Brenda Maddox: *Maggie. The first lady* (Hodder & Stoughton, London, 2003)

Alister McGrath, with Joanna Collicutt McGrath: *The Dawkins Delusion. Atheist fundamentalism and the denial of the divine* (SPCK, London, 2007)

Patricia Murray: *Margaret Thatcher. A Profile* (W H Allen, London, 1980)

Denis Noble: *The Music of Life. Biology beyond the Genome* (OUP, Oxford, 2006)

Eric E Rich: *The Education Act 1870. A study of public opinion* (Longmans, London, 1970)

Bernd Schepeler: *Dialog mit der Kanzlerin. Dient Angela Merkel Deutschland? Ein Personaleignungstest der Anderen Art* (Herstellung und Verlag: Books on Demand GmbH, Norderstedt; Umschlaggestaltung, Wehry-Druck OHG, Untermassfeld, 2007)

Simon Singh & Edzard Ernst: *Trick or Treatment? Alternative medicine on trial* (Bantam Press, London, 2008)

J C Smuts: *Jan Christian Smuts* (Cassell, London, 1952); a biography by Smuts's son

C P Snow: *The Two Cultures and the Scientific Revolution. The Rede Lecture, 1959* (Cambridge University Press, Cambridge, 1959)

Margaret Thatcher: *The Path to Power* (HarperCollins, London, 1995)

Margaret Thatcher: *Statecraft. Strategies for a Changing World* (HarperCollins, London, 2002)

Damian Thompson: *Counterknowledge. How we surrendered to conspiracy theories, quack medicine, bogus science and fake history* (Atlantic Books, London, 2008)

Horace Annesley Vachell: *Blinkers. A Romance of the Preconceived Idea* (Cassell and Company, Limited, London, 1921)

Frans de Waal: *Our Inner Ape. The best and worst of human nature* (Granta Books, London, 2005)

Gabrielle Walker and Sir David King: *The Hot Topic. How to tackle global warming and still keep the lights on* (Bloomsbury, London, 2008)

Francis Wheen: *How Mumbo-Jumbo Conquered the World. A short history of modern delusions* (Fourth Estate, London, 2004)

Index

Page numbers in **bold** refer to illustrations; page numbers in *italic* refer to endnotes